The Field Guide to Physician Coding

SECOND EDITION

Betsy Nicoletti, MS, CPC

Founder, Codapedia.com

GREENBRANCH
PUBLISHING

Phoenix, Maryland

Published by Greenbranch Publishing, LLC
PO Box 208
Phoenix, MD 21131
Phone: (800) 933-3711
Fax: (410) 329-1510
Email: info@greenbranch.com
Websites: www.greenbranch.com, www.soundpractice.net, www.codapedia.com

Greenbranch Publishing books are available at special quantity discounts to use as premiums and sales promotions, or for use in corporate training programs. For more information, please write to the Director of Special Sales, Greenbranch Publishing, PO Box 208, Phoenix, MD 21131 or (800) 933-3711 or info@greenbranch.com.

This publication is designed to provide general medical practice management information and is sold with the understanding that neither the author nor the publisher is engaged in rendering legal, accounting, ethical, or clinical advice. While all information in this document is believed to be correct at the time of writing, no warranty, express or implied, is made as to its accuracy as information may change over time. If legal or other expert advice is required, the services of a competent professional person should be sought.

CPT® is a registered trademark of the American Medical Association

Printed in the United States of America by United Book Press, Inc. www.unitedbookpress.com

PUBLISHER
Nancy Collins

EDITORIAL ASSISTANT
Jennifer Weiss

BOOK DESIGNER
Laura Carter
Carter Publishing Studio

COPYEDITOR
Jennifer Schmidt

INDEXER
Anne Seitz

Table of Contents

Dedication

Many friends and colleagues helped and encouraged me in writing this book. Nancy Collins, the publisher at Greenbranch, was enthusiastic and flexible. Working with her was terrific. Nancy and I recently joined forces on a new venture, www.codapedia.com. Codapedia is a wiki about physician reimbursement and coding. Visit www.codapedia.com for free coding information on a variety of topics.

My friend, Jock Alman, listened endlessly as I talked about the ups and downs of writing this. He was steady and supportive throughout, while providing a counterbalance to my unbridled enthusiasm. He recently supported me through the recovery of a broken ankle, during which I was able to revise this book.

Bob and Sally Anderson were there when I first started as a consultant, and we discussed entrepreneurial matters large and small over countless dinners.

My former boss, Dave Pagniucci, started me on this road to success.

I am grateful to Elizabeth Woodcock for writing the foreword to the first edition. I can't express how much I respect her work. I recently had the opportunity to work with Elizabeth on an educational project and remain impressed with her knowledge, dedication and attention to detail that ensures success.

Nancy Maguire generously wrote the foreword to this edition. She is presently preparing ICD-10 Education for the Codapedia community. Many thanks to her! (www.codapedia.com)

Although I had the idea for *The Field Guide to Physician Coding* for months, there would be no book without my participation in the Strategic Coach™ program. Thank you to Teresa Easler, Kelly Sickmeir, and the founder, Dan Sullivan. Without the principles of focusing on those activities that get me results, I would never have finished this book.

And to my three wonderful children, Dave, Dan, and Julie Allen, I send my special thanks and love.

BETSY NICOLETTI

About the Author

 Betsy Nicoletti is an author, speaker and consultant. She is the owner of Medical Practice Consulting, a consulting firm whose mission is to help doctors get paid. Besides doing auditing and compliance work, she excels at making complicated coding concepts easy for clinicians to understand and use. She holds a Masters in Organization and Management from Antioch New England and has worked in and around physician offices for over 20 years. (www.mpconsulting.org)

Betsy was the Chief Operating Officer of Network Management Services in Springfield, Vermont for nine years. During that time, she was responsible for physician practice operations in the network and the operations of the MSO administrative service functions. She set up a centralized billing and information system that served over 20 practices and 60 physicians. She organized the management services and was responsible for operational systems including personnel, regulatory compliance, budgeting, and planning.

An experienced auditor of Evaluation and Management services, Betsy educates physicians on coding, billers in billing, and auditors in auditing. She speaks locally and nationally on coding and documentation, A/R management and physician profitability.

She is the author of the *Physician Auditing Workbook*, published by DecisionHealth. Her speaking engagements include Greenbranch Publishing, Pri-Med, MGMA, ACHE, DecisionHealth, HFMA and World Research Group. Her articles are published in the *Journal of Medical Practice Management*®, *Family Practice Management*, *Physicians Practice Journal* and *Medical Economics*. She is a member of the National Speakers Association. With Greenbranch Publishing, she founded www.codapedia.com in 2009.

Foreword

This book is intended to be a useful introduction to and resource for navigating the arena of practice management and physician coding. *The Field Guide to Physician Coding, Second Edition* is unique because it sets the foundation for managing accounts receivable and aging reports as well as easy to understand coding and billing rules.

This book is not simply a review and comparison of coding concepts; it is based on years of physician practice management and "in the trenches" knowledge experienced by Betsy Nicoletti.

Betsy understands the pinnacle of the coding philosophy that stands for ethical and accurate coding principles as presented in this manual. The subjects covered include the range of legislative requirements for coding frequently performed services in the physician office and hospital settings. The key points discussed will leave you with a clear understanding of the issues at hand as well as additional resources to explore the topics (like giving the reader a fishing pole for self-inquiry).

Coding is an art (skill or mastery) as well as a science (knowledge as distinguished from ignorance or misunderstanding), and this book delivers on both. The Billing and Coding rules presented are right on and will serve as safeguards to prevent claim denials and refiling. Physicians and coding staff alike are barraged every day with complex rules and code changes, and this can be very stressful. *The Field Guide to Physician Coding, Second Edition* will ease that stress by delivering the facts in language we can all understand.

Citations are a valuable addition to each chapter and will further support the rules and key points discussed. This Guide is a valuable and practical addition to the physician's and coder's library, and I highly recommend and applaud the time and effort spent in development.

NANCY MAGUIRE, ACS, HCS-P

Introduction

P hysician coding is important for two reasons: coding drives revenue and compliance requires accurate coding. Physician payment depends on correct coding, an effective billing process, and payer reimbursement policies.

What are these three components?

Coding is the process of assigning a procedure code, (CPT® or HCPCS code) and a diagnosis code (ICD-9 DM) to a physician service that accurately describes what the physician did for or to the patient, and the patient's condition or the reason for the service. It includes rules for the use of modifiers and description of multiple procedures.

Billing is the processes of sending a claim form or invoice to the patient or third party payer for the service provided and collecting for those services.

Reimbursement is the payment for physician services and is dependent on government rules and policies, third party rules and policies, and mandated and associated fee schedules.

The source of rules and policies for all three aspects of collecting the fee in the physician office are multiple. Some definitions are developed by the American Medical Association. Congress mandates some rules. Payment policies vary by third party payers and even between Medicare carriers. The CMS website is a rich and robust source of data, but the answer to a question can be hard to find on this website.

Purpose

The Field Guide to Physician Coding, Second Edition provides answers to common coding questions. I draw on definitions from the AMA and some coding and payment policies in use by Medicare and many commercial payers. My goal in this book is to provide a resource that is quick and easy to use. The alphabetic format means a clinician, coder, or biller can quickly locate the topic and answer a question. Each topic entry follows a consistent format: definition, explanation, codes, coverage, billing and coding rules, key points, see also other entries, and citation. The citation is important for users who want more details or need to want to read the rules from the official source.

Topic selection

I included topics that come up over and over again in my work with physicians. Over the course of a year, I meet with and speak to thousands of physicians, nurse practitioners, and physician assistants, both one-on-one and in groups. Their questions serve as the basis for the topics in this book. It is a resource for my clients and for all of the other clinicians and coders and billers with whom I don't meet.

CPT® Companion

The Field Guide to Physician Coding, Second Edition will not replace your up-to-date copies of the CPT®, HCPCS, and ICD-9 books. All offices must buy these resources yearly. You may need to refer to those resources as you read the answers in this book.

Citations

A website address or other resource is the citation for each entry. These addresses are up-to-date as we go to press. URLs change from time to time. The quickest method I know to find data on a government website is by using a new Google feature that searches only government websites. Paste the citation or topic into this specialized search engine. http://www.google.com/ig/usgov

I have not included CPT® citations from either the *CPT® Assistant* or *CPT® Changes: An Insider's View*. These citations are available in the professional addition of the CPT® book. *The CPT® Assistant* is a monthly journal published by the AMA. *CPT® Changes: An Insider's View* is an annual AMA publication that explains in more detail changes made to CPT® codes that year. Both are copyrighted and are the product of the American Medical Association. I strongly suggest that all physician practices purchase at least one copy of the professional edition of the CPT® book and subscribe to the CPT® Assistant for more information on CPT® definitions and codes.

Collecting for physician services is hard work. I am constantly impressed with the dedication, knowledge and perseverance of physician office staff members, who do this job every day. I hope this book is helpful to you!

BETSY NICOLETTI

Accounts Receivable Benchmark Data

Definition:
> Accounts receivable benchmark data measure a physician practice's performance in collecting money for professional services rendered.

Explanation:
> Most physician practices collect only a fraction of the money for services performed at the time of services. This is because practices participate with Medicare, Medicaid, and other third party insurance companies, and these companies must process the claim before paying the practice for the service. *It is important to monitor the progress of a practice in collecting these monies that are owed to it monthly and on a year-to-date basis. Payments from patients at the time of service, however, become more important each year.*

Codes: All.

Coverage: All.

Billing and coding rules:
> Practices can collect from self pay patients at the time of service. Co-pays should be collected at the time of service as well. Typically, the coinsurance and deductible amount are collected from the patient after the claim has been processed rather than at the time of service. However, with the availability of online eligibility and benefit verification, practices can know at the time of service the amount of the patient's deductible and coinsurance amount. That is, at the time of the visit, the practice can know the patient due portion and collect it at the time of service. As patients now have higher out of pocket limits, this is critical. Third-party payments are received from the practice between ten days and 60 days after the service is rendered, or longer. It is important to monitor the A/R benchmarks to see what kind of a job the practice is doing in this collection process.
>
> The most common accounts receivable benchmarks are gross collection ratio, adjusted collection ratio, days in receivables outstanding, and the aging report.

Related issues:
> The easiest money ever made in physician practice comes from collecting money for services already performed rather than asking physicians to

work harder or perform more services. It is critical for practices to collect efficiently and effectively for the services they are already providing. Although each step in this process is easy, there are many steps, and the way the steps work together is very complex.

Key points:

- Monitor performance on the A/R benchmarks monthly and on a year-to-date basis.
- Compare these benchmarks with standards from a national organization.
- Administration monitors physician productivity, but is equally important to monitor the practice's effectiveness in collections.
- Use practice management software or a clearinghouse service to verify eligibility, benefits and patient due amounts before the patient arrives at the office.

See also: Gross Collection Ratio, Adjusted Collection Ratio, Aging Report, Days in Accounts Receivable.

Citation:

Medical Group Management Association (www.mgma.com).

Deborah L. Walker, Elizabeth W. Woodcock, Sara M. Larch, *The Physician Billing Process: 12 Potholes to Avoid in the Road to Getting Paid, Second Edition, 2009.*

Practice Support Resources (www.practicesupport.com)

Adjusted Collection Ratio

Definition:

The adjusted collection ratio compares cash collected to net charges. Net charges are the difference between gross charges and the required government and third party adjustments that a practice must take based on their contracts and fee allowances. To calculate the ratio, divide cash collected by net charges. To do this, a practice must know gross charges, insurance adjustments and cash collections for the same time period. Depending on the specialty, physician practices set a goal for the adjusted collection ratio of 90% to 96%.

Explanation:

When a practice signs contracts with third party payers and participates with Medicare and Medicaid, the practice agrees that the payer fee schedule will be the amount collected from the payer and the patient combined. Net charges represent the difference between what a practice bills and what it is allowed to collect. To calculate net charges, subtract the mandated third party adjustments from the gross charges. Then, divide the cash collections for the same period by the net charges to calculate the adjusted collection ratio.

> Net collections = Gross charges—mandated adjustments.
> Adjusted Collection ratio = Cash/net collections.

The adjusted collection ratio measures the performance of accounts receivable better than the gross collection ratio, because it reflects mandated adjustments: money that the practice could not have collected based on its contracts. Practices should watch what is written off in the adjustment category in order to know if this measurement is accurate.

Codes: All.

Coverage: All payers.

Billing and coding rules:

The adjustments in these insurance categories should include only adjustments the practice must take based on the fee schedule and contract. Do not include write offs for bad debt, charity care, eligibility or registration errors, or coding errors.

Related issues:

Compare this benchmark calculation by specialty with other practices of the same specialty. This data is available from some specialty societies or can be purchased from the Medical Group Management Association.

Key points:

- Calculate the adjusted collection ratio monthly and year-to-date. Some practices calculate it every three or six months.
- Watch what is written off as contractual. If a practice includes in the contractual adjustment amounts that could have been collected, then this will distort the calculation.
- Do not allow coding errors or incorrect denials to be written off incorrectly as adjustments.

See also: Account receivable benchmarks, gross collection rate, days in accounts receivable, aging report.

Citation:

Medical Group Management Association (www.mgma.com).

Practice Support Resources (www.practicesupport.com)

Advance Beneficiary Notice

Definition:

An Advance Beneficiary Notice (ABN) is a written notification that a physician gives to a patient before providing a service that may not be covered or will not be covered by Medicare.

Explanation:

Medicare instituted the patient notification rules to protect their beneficiaries from financial liability when receiving a service that is not or may not be covered by Medicare. This written notice must be given to the patient prior to the patient's preparation for that service and must specifically inform the patient of the reason that the service may not or will not be covered. Practices can not use blanket or blank ABNs.

Code: An ABN may be needed for many services.

Coverage:

ABNs are specific to Medicare, although some third party payers have similar limit of liability rules.

Billing and coding rules:

The first requirement for an ABN is to use the form approved by CMS. CMS revised the ABN form, and mandated the use of the new form starting March 1, 2009. Use form CMS-R-131. Forms ABN-G and ABN-L are no longer valid.

A practice must execute the ABN properly prior to patient preparation for the service; the patient must not be asked to sign an ABN after being gowned and prepped to receive the service or after the service has commenced or the specimen has been drawn.

When completing the ABN, the specific name and description of the service must be listed. "Lab test:" is not specific. "CBC" is specific.

The reason that the practice believes the service may not be covered must also be specifically listed on the ABN. It is insufficient to write "Medicare may not cover this service." If the ABN is non-specific, such as "Medicare may not cover the service," the practice may not hold the patient financially responsible. Examples of specific reasons might be "Medicare does not pay for an EKG for your condition" or "Medicare only pays for a pelvic exam every two years for a patient with no known risk factors, and your most recent pelvic exam was one year ago."

A family member can sign an ABN if the patient is unable to do so. If the patient refuses to sign the ABN, but insists on receiving the service, a staff member should note this on the ABN and a second staff member should witness it.

Medicare typically requires ABNs for procedures when the diagnoses are not listed as covered on either a National Coverage Determination (NCD) or a Local Coverage Determination (LCD), formerly known as Local Medical Review Policies (LMRPs). Healthcare procedures or services with an NCD or LCD have a list of indications for which the service is covered. If the patient's condition is not covered, then an ABN is needed.

An ABN establishes financial liability for a service. If a practice uses an ABN, it may hold the patient financially responsible for the service it is providing. Without it, the practice or lab providing the service can not bill the patient if Medicare denies the claim. Medicare wants to make sure that the patient is making an informed decision about whether or not to receive the service, prior to receiving it.

The practice is required to keep the original of each ABN in the practice and give the patient a copy.

Related issues:

When submitting a claim to Medicare, there are three modifiers to indicate the status of that claim in relation to an ABN.

GA: Waiver of liability statement issued as required by payer policy. Patient is responsible for charge.

GX: Notice of liability issued, voluntary under payer policy. Use for non-covered services, which will be denied.

GY: Item or service statutorily excluded or does not meet the definition of any Medicare benefit

GZ: Item or service expected to be denied as not reasonable or necessary. Using GZ tells the Medicare carrier that no ABN is on file.

Understanding medical necessity as defined by an NCD or an LCD is key for use of ABNs. Use an ABN when those policies indicate that the patient's condition is not covered for that service or may not be covered. ABNs are not required for services that are never covered by Medicare; this includes cosmetic services and routine preventive services.

According to Medicare's manual instructions for ABNs, there are some citations that do not require ABNs. Here is what it says:

> ABNs are not required for care that is either statutorily excluded from coverage under Medicare (i.e., care that is never covered) or fails to meet a technical benefit requirement (i.e., lacks required certification). However, the ABN can be issued voluntarily in place of the Notice of Exclusion from Medicare Benefits (NEMB) for care that is never covered such as:
>
> - Care that fails to meet the definition of a Medicare benefit as defined in §1861 of the Social Security Act.
> - Care that is explicitly excluded from coverage under §1862 of the Social Security Act.
>
> Examples include:
> - Services for which there is no legal obligation to pay;
> - Services paid for by a government entity other than Medicare (this exclusion does not include services paid for by Medicaid on behalf of dual-eligibles);
> - Services required as a result of war;
> - Personal comfort items;
> - Routine physicals and most screening tests;
> - Routine eye care;
> - Dental care; and
> - Routine foot care.

Key points:
- Use ABN form CMS-R-131.
- Execute the ABN prior to preparing the patient for the service.
- Describe the service specifically.
- Describe specifically the reason the service may not or will not be covered.
- Blanket ABNs are not legal.
- Blank ABNs are not legal.
- Submit with the appropriate GA, GX, GY, or GZ modifier.
- A practice may only hold patients financially responsible if they have properly executed an ABN.

See also: Medical necessity, local coverage determinations, national coverage determinations.

Citations:

ABN forms and information are available at http://cms.gov/medicare/bni/

CMS, Medicare Claims Processing Manual, Pub 100-04, Chapter 30, Section 50, https://www.cms.gov/Manuals/IOM/

Aging Report

Definition:

An aging report of accounts receivable breaks down total accounts receivable by the aging for each charge, which is the number of days from the date of service to the current date.

Explanation:

The aging of a practice's accounts receivable is typically done in 30 day increments. These are current, 31 to 60 days, 91 to 120 days, 121 to 150 days, and over 150 days. The report can serve as an excellent benchmark to assess the performance of the practice's billing, coding, and collection staff. It is also a good measure of the speed of your third party and patient due payments.

The norms for this vary widely by specialty. Practices with large workers compensation or third party liability cases will have a higher percentage of their receivables in the over-120 days category. A good goal is to have less than 20% of your accounts receivable over 120 days. As receivables age, the practice is less likely to be able to collect them.

Codes: All.

Coverage: All.

Billing and coding rules:

The accuracy of charge posting, registration, correct coding, and the ability to submit clean, edited claims all effect this measure.

Related issues:

Including the credit balances in the report will decrease the true percentage of claims over 120 days and in every other category. Run the aging report without credit balances included. If possible, run this report by date of service rather than by the date the claim is re-submitted. If a claim ages by the date it is resubmitted, the age of the receivables seems lower.

A/R systems can show this data in summary and in detail. For the purposes of accounts receivable benchmarking, look at the summary data. However, this data by payer class and in detail are good tools to follow up on past due accounts. Tracking A/R by payer class in summary will also measure how quickly individual payers process and pay claims.

Key points:

- Look at the aging report monthly for the entire practice and by payer class.
- Keep track of the percentage of claims that are over 120 days old. An increase in this percentage indicates a problem with claims submission or payer promptness.
- Large credit balances will provide false information about the percentages of claims in each category. Run the aging report without credit balances and using the date of service (not the date the claim was submitted or re-submitted) for each claim.
- Norms for your specialty can be found at your specialty society or bought from the Medical Group Management Association.

See also: Gross collection ratio, adjusted collection ratio, days in accounts receivable.

Citation:

Medical Group Management Association (www.mgma.com).

Practice Support Resources (www.practicesupport.com)

Allergen Immunotherapy

Definition:

Allergen immunotherapy is the provision of serum allergy treatment to patients who have hypersensitivity to one or more allergens.

Explanation:

There are three sets of services described by the codes in the CPT® book:

1. Administration of allergen immunotherapy, which is the set of codes to be used when the physician injects the allergen into a patient.
2. Preparing the allergens, single or multiple doses, and administering the serum.
3. Preparation of the allergens.

Codes:

95115 and 95117 are for the administration of the allergens.

95120 through 95134 are for the provision of the allergens and injections. These are combined codes and include both the preparation of the allergen and the injection of it. Medicare does not cover these codes.

95144 is used when the allergist prepares a single dose of an allergen rather than preparing the allergen in multi-dose vials.

95145 through 95170 are used for the preparation of multiple doses, based on the number of planned doses the patient requires.

Coverage:

Many Medicare carriers have LCDs for these services. These services are provided to patients who have type 1 immediate hypersensitivity to one or more allergens.

Payment policies and the use of these codes vary among third parties. Medicare rules are explained below. For services to non-Medicare patients, it is advisable to ask your third party representative for the coverage policies.

Billing rules:

There are two injection codes, 95115 for a single injection of an allergen, and 95117 for two or more injections. Be careful about the units with these codes, as only one unit should be billed for either 95115 or 95117. The code 95115 is a component code of 95117 and would never be billed to the same patient on the same day. So bill 95115 if you give a single injection to a patient; but if you give two, three, or ten allergy injections on a single date to a patient, bill 95117 with one unit.

Code 95144 is for the preparation of a single vial dosage of allergen for a patient. It is typically covered only when the physician who is preparing the allergen is not going to give that dosage. If a physician were going to give the dosage him- or herself, the physician would prepare a larger, multiple dose vial and not a single dose vial. For example, you would use this code for a patient who was traveling out of the state or out of the country and was going to carry one dose to be administered at his or her destination.

Codes 95145 through 95170 should be used when preparing multiple dose vials of allergens. Bill based on the number of planned doses prepared. Sometimes the patient's dosage may vary; don't make adjustments for that, but bill for the number of planned doses.

Codes 95120 to 95134 describe the provision of the allergen and the administration of it. Medicare does not pay for these bundled services even though they describe two separate components. Medicare requires practices to bill for those separately using the 95115 to 95117 series of codes and the provision/preparation using the 95145 to 95170 series of codes. Check with your third party payers for coverage provisions and billing rules.

What about providing an office visit on the same day as an allergy injection? The allergy injections are not bundled into the office visit codes. If you have provided a distinct, significant, separately identifiable service on the same day as an allergy injection, you may use a 25 modifier on the office visit.

The key here is that the service represented by the office visit should be a distinct, separately identifiable one. For example, a patient may be treated for another illness not related to the allergy on the same day as an allergy shot. The patient could be treated for an allergy related illness. However, in that case, be sure that the history, exam and medical decision making justifies the level of office visit and the level of E/M service that you are billing on the same day that you are billing for the administration of the allergy shot.

Do not bill a 99211 (a nurse visit) routinely either in place of the allergy shot or in addition to the allergy shot. Some practices say that their policy is that all patients need evaluations by the nurse on the same day as they receive their allergy shots. This evaluation is considered part of the payment for the administration of the allergen. It would not be appropriate to routinely bill a nurse visit on the same day as an allergy shot. (Remember that if you are billing for a nurse visit to a Medicare patient, that nurse visit must meet all of the requirements of incident to billing.)

Key points:

- Be careful about units for both the administration codes and the dosages provided.
- Remember that 95115 is a component code of 95117 and can never be billed in addition to it.
- When billing code 95117, use only one unit.
- Medicare does not pay for the series of codes that describes both prescribing and preparing the allergen and provision of the allergen (95120 to 95134).
- 95144, which is provision of a single dose of the allergen, is billable as long as that dosage is going to be given in another provider's office and there is medical necessity for preparing a single dose.
- Use codes 95145 to 95170 for multiple dose preparation. Bill based on the planned number of doses.
- Be careful about billing a nurse visit with an allergy injection. Although 99211 and 95115 are not bundled procedures, the nurse visit should represent a distinct service from the assessment of a patient before and after an allergy shot.
- All E/M services billed on the same day as an allergy injection must meet the criteria of a distinct, significant, separately identifiably E/M service with a 25 modifier on the office visit.

See also: Nurse visits, immunization administration, injections and infusions.

Citation:

CMS, *Medicare Claims Processing Manual*, Pub 100–04, Chapter 12, Section 200, http://www.cms.hhs.gov/Manuals/IOM/list.asp

Assistant at Surgery Services

Definition:

Assistant at surgery services are services provided by a surgical assistant during a surgical procedure. Assistant at surgery services are payable by Medicare and other third parties for certain surgeries.

Explanation:

One of the indicators in the Medicare Physician Fee Schedule Data Base (MPFSDB) is for the assistant at surgery. Each CPT® and Healthcare Common Procedures Coding System (HCPCS) code in the MPFSDB has an assistant at surgery indicator. Here is the key to these four indicators.

> 0 = Payment restriction for assistants at surgery applies to this procedure unless supporting documentation is submitted to establish medical necessity.

> 1 = Statutory payment restriction for assistants at surgery applies to this procedure. Assistant at surgery may not be paid.

> 2 = Payment restriction for assistants at surgery does not apply to this procedure. Assistant at surgery may be paid.

> 9 = Concept does not apply.

Codes:

The modifiers used to report assistant at surgery services are:

> 80   Assistant surgeon

> 81   Minimum assistant surgeon

> 82   Assistant surgeon (when qualified resident surgeon not available). Modifier 82 is used in teaching facilities.

> AS   Physician assistant, nurse practitioner, or clinical nurse specialist services for assistant at surgery

Coverage:

These indicators are in the MPFSDB but are typically followed by other third party payers.

Billing and coding rules:

Bill the assistant at surgery services using the CPT® code billed by the primary surgeon and appending the appropriate modifier to the code.

Medicare allows 16% of the allowed amount for the primary surgery as payment for the assistant at surgery services. Commercial payers typically pay between 20 and 25% of the allowed amount for the primary surgeon. It is common for practices to set their fee for their assistant at surgery services at 25% of the fee that they charge for their primary surgical services.

If the assistant at surgery indicator on the MPDBFS does not allow for an assistant at surgery, you are prohibited by Medicare from billing the patient for the service. Most third party payer contracts also prohibit this. Most third party payers follow the same assistant at surgery rules, although some have developed a different listing.

Related issues:

The condition of some patients may require an assistant at surgery, even for surgeries when this is not typically covered. A physician may bill for an assistant at surgery for surgery codes with a 0 indicator on the MPFSDB. The physician must document the medical necessity for this and send this documentation to the payer. This would include the patient's medical conditions, co-morbidity, or increased risk that necessitated the need for a surgical assistant.

Key points:

- Check the MPFSDB for the procedure and see if the assistant at surgery is allowed. If so, bill with a CPT® code of the primary surgeon, appending the appropriate modifier.
- If a Non-Physician Practitioner (NPP) provides the assistant at surgery care for a Medicare patient, use the AS modifier.
- When billing for a code with a zero indicator, which means that supporting documentation must be required for payment, be sure to indicate the reason that the assistant at surgeon was required for this service.

See also: Global surgical package, Medicare physician fee schedule data base.

Citation:

CMS, *Medicare Claims Processing Manual*, Pub. 100–04, Chapter 12, Section 20.4.3, http://www.cms.hhs.gov/Manuals/IOM/list.asp

Care Plan Oversight – CPT® Codes (Non-Medicare)

Definition:

Care Plan Oversight (CPO) is a non face-to-face service provided by a physician for a patient who requires complex, multi-disciplinary care.

Explanation:

These codes are used by physicians to describe coordination of care for patients who are under the care of a home health agency (HHA) hospice, or a skilled nursing facility (SNF). The patients must require complex supervision and management. Low intensity or infrequent supervision services are considered part of the pre and post work of face-to-face evaluation and management (E/M) services. These time-based codes are billed per calendar months.

Codes: 99374 to 99380.

Coverage:

These codes have zero relative value units (RVUs) in the MPFSDB and so are not covered by Medicare. Many private payers, however, will pay them.

Billing and coding rules:

These codes are time based codes described by the care the patient is receiving, (HHA, hospice, or SNF); and by time, 15 to 29 minutes or 30 minutes or more. Whenever time is used to select a CPT® code, time must be documented in the medical record as well as on the billing sheets.

Many practices find using log sheets useful to document this service. Each entry on the log sheet should include the date of service, a brief description of the nature of the supervision and the coordination, the amount of time spent on the patient, and the initials of the clinician providing the service.

The physician should document this information whenever supervision is performed.

At the end of the calendar month, if the threshold time of 15 minutes is met, bill for the service. These codes are for the work of the physician only and are not to be used for staff time. Nurses, medical assistants, or other employees of the physicians may not provide this service.

Only one physician should report this service in any calendar month for a particular patient.

The patient must require complex review of the care plan and condition, and this must require multiple phone calls, data review unrelated to an E/M service, and discussion with other healthcare providers.

The definition of these codes, unlike the Medicare HCPCS care plan oversight codes, allows the provider to bill for time spent discussing the patient's condition with family members, legal guardians, or other care givers.

Related issues:

Most insurance companies will not pay for telephone calls, record review, or any non-face-to-face service time with a patient. Care plan oversight is one of the few covered services for a non-face-to-face service.

Key points:

- Use these codes for non-Medicare patients. Medicare uses HCPCS codes to describe services similar to these.
- Document time spent, what was done, and the dates the service was performed. Initial each entry and sign the log at the end of the month.
- Bill for a calendar month with a start and end date as the first and last date of the month.
- Include only provider time.
- Only one provider per month may bill for this service.
- Put the home health agency or hospice UPIN on the claim form.

See also: Care plan oversight for Medicare patients.

Citation:

CMS, *Medicare Claims Processing Manual*, Pub 100–4, Chapter 12, Section 180, http://www.cms.gov/Manuals/IOM/list.asp

Care Plan Oversight for Medicare Patients

Definition:

Care plan oversight (CPO) is the supervision of a patient receiving Medicare covered home health agency (HHA) or hospice services who requires supervision for complex and multi-disciplinary treatment.

Explanation:

Medicare developed these care plan services to pay physicians and NPPs for providing complex treatment supervision to patients who require coordination of multi-disciplinary care. It allows a provider to be paid for non-face-to-face services, when these services are greater than 30 minutes in a calendar month, the patient's condition is complex, and significant coordination of care is required.

Codes:

These services are defined and billed to Medicare using the following codes.

G0181: physician supervision of a patient receiving Medicare-covered services provided by a participating home health agency (patient not present) requiring complex and multidisciplinary care modalities involving regular physician development and/or revision of care plans, review of subsequent reports of patient status, review of laboratory and other studies, communication (including telephone calls) with other healthcare professionals involved in the patient's care, integration of new information into the medical treatment plan and/or adjustment of medical therapy, within a calendar month, 30 minutes or more.

G0182: physician supervision of a patient receiving Medicare-covered services provided by a participating Hospice (patient not present) requiring complex and multidisciplinary care modalities involving regular physician development and/or revision of care plans, review of subsequent reports of patient status, review of laboratory and other studies, communication (including telephone calls) with other healthcare professionals involved in the patient's care, integration of new information into the medical treatment plan and/or adjustment of medical therapy, within a calendar month, 30 minutes or more.

Coverage:

Medicare beneficiaries. Check with commercial payers to see if they cover the CPT® CPO codes or the HCPCS codes.

Billing and coding rules:

The coding rules for this service are detailed and specific. Many physicians provide this service without ever billing for it. CPO is on the 2006 Work Plan of the Office of Inspector General.

Time spent in the coordination activities must be documented in the medical record, along with a brief description of the work performed, the date of the work, and the signature of the provider. The services must be provided by the same physician who certified the patient and signed the form for HHA or hospice services. A qualified NPP may provide CPO if that NPP has a collaborative agreement with the physician who signed the certification for home health agency or hospice services.

The physician providing the service may not be an employee or director, paid or voluntary, of the home health agency or hospice providing the care or have any significant financial arrangement with those organizations.

Only one physician in a month may provide and be paid for CPO. In order to bill for CPO, the physician must have seen the patient and billed for an E/M service within the last six months. The physician or NPP must provide 30 minutes of CPO in a calendar month.

In addition to receiving home health agency or hospice service, the beneficiary must require complex, multi-disciplinary supervision to manage his or her care.

According to the Medicare claims processing manual, you can bill for CPO for time spent on the following activities:
- Regular physician development and/or revision of care plan
- Review of subsequent reports of patient's status
- Review of related or laboratory or other studies
- Communication with other healthcare professionals not employed in the same practice who are involved in the patient's care
- Integration of new information into the medical treatment plan
- Adjustment of medical therapy.

The activities below may not be counted in the time billed for CPO:
- Time spent discussing the patient's care with the physician's own staff member
- Time spent for any staff member activities
- Time spent in discussing the patient's care with the patient's family member or caregiver. This is a distinction between the Medicare defined HCPCS code and the CPT® definition of care plan oversight.
- The routine renewal of drug prescriptions

- The review of diagnostic test results related to an E/M service
- Travel time, time spent in submitting claims, or time spent calculating CPO time
- Time and work spent in providing discharge services, including 99217, 99238, and 99239
- Post-op care in the global period

Bill with the first and last calendar date of the month on the claim form and include the UPIN/NPI of the home health agency or hospice organization on your claim form.

The NPP may bill for CPO services, however, they may not certify the plan of care. The Internet Only Manual (IOM) Section 100-4, Chapter 12, Section 180, A: Home Health CPO states:

> "Non-physician practitioners can perform CPO services only if the physician signing the plan of care provides ongoing care under the same plan of care as does the NPP billing for CPO and either:
> - The physician and NPP are part of the same group practice; or
> - The NPP is a nurse practitioner or clinical nurse specialist, the physician signing the plan of care also has a collaborative agreement with the NPP; or
> - The NPP is a physician assistant, the physician signing the plan of care is also the physician who provides general supervision of physician assistant services for the practice.
>
> Billing may be made for care plan oversight services furnished by an NPP when:
> - The NPP providing the care plan oversight has seen and examined the patient;
> - The NPP providing the care plan oversight is not functioning as a consultant whose participation is limited to a single medical condition rather than multidisciplinary coordination of care; and
> - The NPP providing the care plan oversight integrates his or her care with that of the physician who signed the plan of care."

Related issues:

This is one of the few services allowing physicians to be paid for non-face-to-face time. Typically, time spent on phone calls, coordination of care, and record review are considered part of the pre- and post work of evaluation and management services.

Key points:

- Document time, a brief description of the nature of the activity, and the date the service was performed. Sign the documentation.
- Patients receiving Medicare covered home health agency or hospice service are eligible for this benefit.
- The patient must require supervision of complex multi-disciplinary care.
- Only one physician may bill for CPO time in a month. It must be the same physician who certified the patient for home health agency or hospice care.
- An NPP may provide CPO services when the NPP has a collaborative agreement with the physician who certified the patient for home health agency care or hospice services.
- Review the list of services that may be included in time.
- Remember that the physician must have no financial arrangement with and may not be a voluntary director of the hospice or home health agency.

See also: Care plan oversight, CPT® codes.

Citation:

CMS, *Medicare Claims Processing Manual*, Pub 100-4, Chapter 12, Section 180, http://www.cms.hhs.gov/Manuals/IOM/list.asp

Certification of Home Health Services

Definition:

Medicare pays physicians for the work required to plan and review Medicare covered home health services for patients.

Explanation:

In 2001, Medicare added coverage to pay physicians for creating and reviewing care plans for patients receiving Medicare covered home health services. The initial certification may be billed once, when the patient has not received home health services in the past 60 days. The re-certification may be billed 60 days after the initial certification.

Codes:

G0179: Physician re-certification for Medicare covered home health services under a home health plan of care (patient not present). This includes contacts with the home health agency and review of patient status reports required to affirm the initial implementation of the plan of care, per re-certification period.

G0180: Physician certification for Medicare-covered home health services under a home health plan of care (patient not present). This includes contacts with the home health agency and review of patient status reports required to affirm the initial implementation of the plan of care, per certification period.

Coverage:

Medicare beneficiaries receiving Medicare covered home health services. Only a physician may bill for this service.

Billing and coding rules:

The physician who provides this service may not be an employee of the home health agency or have a significant financial or contractual relationship with the home health agency.

Physicians must create and review the plan of care and the data collected by the home health agency and maintain a record of this in their own medical record. The home health agency may not simply prepare the plan for physician signature and maintain the certification in its own record.

Physician work that is related to and billed as care plan oversight must be separate and distinct from the work of this certification. CMS will not pay for the certification and care plan oversight for the same minutes in the month. A physician may provide and bill for an E/M service in the same month as the certification for home healthcare certification. The time spent in the home health certification should be distinct from the pre- and post work of the visit, and from the visit itself.

Document in the physician's medical record the creation of the plan and the distinct work of the certification. For example, the plan for a progress note might include a discussion of the patient's need for home health services and a brief description of the plan of care. The physician's office should keep a copy of the certification and re-certification in its own chart, as well as documentation of phone calls and data review from the home health agency.

NPPs may not bill for these services.

Unlike care plan oversight, there is no minimum time spent in a calendar month to meet the requirements of this code. Physicians need to provide a face-to-face service with a patient prior to certifying them for home healthcare.

Related issues:

Physicians rarely are paid for non-face-to-face services to patients. Billing for certification and re-certification of home health services and care plan oversight are two instances in which they can be paid. The billing and coding rules for each are specific and complex; however, the potential revenue will make it worthwhile for many physician practices to take the time to learn the rules.

Key points:

- Bill for G0179 for the initial home health services certification. It requires that the physician has had a face-to-face service with the patient prior to the certification.
- Bill G0180, the re-certification, after 60 days from the initial certification if the patient remains on home health services and the physician has reviewed the data collected by the home health agency and re-certified the need for the services.
- Physicians with significant financial or contractual arrangements with the home health agency may not bill for this service.
- Document phone calls, data review, and re-certification in the medical record.

- Don't double dip. Physicians cannot be paid for the same time in providing care plan oversight and certification. Both are billable in the same month if the work performed is distinct.

See also: Care plan oversight, care plan oversight for Medicare patients.

Citation:

Federal Register, Vol. 65, No. 212, Nov. 1, 2000, pp. 65406-65408.

http://www.cms.gov/Manuals/IOM/list.asp

Medicare General Information, Eligibility and Entitlement Manual, Chapter 4, Section 30

Medicare Claims Processing Manual, Pub 100-04, Chapter 12, Section 180.1

Cerumen Removal

Definition:

There is a CPT® code for cerumen removal, but payer coverage of this service has varied.

Explanation:

Many practices found that although they billed for cerumen removal at the time of an office visit or physical exam, the service was not paid by most of their payers. In July of 2005 a standard definition of when to bill this service was published in the *CPT® Assistant* and agreed upon by the American Academy of Otolaryngology—Head and Neck Surgery (AAO-HNS).

Code: 69210.

Coverage:

Many payers bundled payments for cerumen removal into the E/M service, regardless of whether or not a 25 modifier was applied to the E/M service. Their claims editing system simply overrode that edit.

Billing and coding rules:

In order to bill 69210, the following criteria must be met per CPT® and the AAO-HNS:

The service must be performed by the physician or NPP, not by a staff member. It is payable only if the cerumen is considered impacted and is removed with a scope and/or wax curettes. Lavage does not meet the criteria for using 69210. The cerumen should be considered impacted only if any one or more of the following are present:

- Visual considerations: Cerumen impairs exam of clinically significant portions of the external auditory canal, tympanic membrane, or middle ear condition.
- Qualitative considerations: Extremely hard, dry, irritative cerumen causes such symptoms as pain, itching, hearing loss, etc.
- Inflammatory considerations: The cerumen is associated with a foul odor, infection, or dermatitis.
- Quantitative considerations: The patient has an obstructive, copious cerumen that cannot be removed without magnification and multiple instrumentations requiring physician skills.

Related issues:

A practice may not bill if a nurse provides this service.

Key points:

- Make sure that the documentation shows that one or more of the above characteristics are met.
- Remember that this service must be performed by a physician or non-physician practitioner.
- If a nurse performs this service, do not bill for it.
- Performing ear lavage is insufficient to bill for and be paid for this service.
- If done on the same day as an E/M service, append modifier 25 to the E/M service. If payment is denied, be prepared to appeal, with the reference and documentation.

See also: Nurse visits.

Citation:

American Academy of Otolaryngology—Head and Neck Surgery, http://www.entlink.net/practice/resources/New-Cerumen-Removal-Code-G0268.cfm

CLIA Waived Tests

Definition:

The Clinical Laboratory Improvement Amendment (CLIA) of 1988 requires that all labs that test human specimens for diagnosis, prevention, or treatment be licensed by the Secretary of Health and Human Services. The amendment also identifies criteria for determining when a test is exempt from regulatory oversight and includes a list of these CLIA waived tests.

Explanation:

There are two types of CLIA waived tests, those performed by a kit, and microscopy tests. CLIA waived tests are typically simple and performed with manufacturer testing kits, which have little risk of error. Kit testing can be performed by a nurse or office assistant/tech with demonstrated competency in test quality control measures. Provider-performed microscopy (PPM) tests are performed on specimens that are not easily transferable and therefore need to be reviewed and read at the time of the patient's visit. Microscopy is a provider (physician) performed test.

Codes:

CMS provides a list of CLIA waived tests on its web site. This listing includes the CPT® code and the description of each manufacturer's testing methodology.

Coverage:

These are covered services if the physician office is enrolled in the CLIA program and has a CLIA waived test certificate.

Billing and coding rules:

CLIA waived lab tests may be performed by physician's lab offices that are enrolled in the CLIA program, that pay a biannual fee, and that follow manufacturer instructions for the tests performed. PPM labs may be performed by physician offices which are enrolled in this program and meet certain quality control and administrative requirements.

Related issues:

Some practices find that they are able to generate significant revenue doing a wider, more complex range of tests. In order to bill more than CLIA waived tests, the practice must be licensed to do so.

Lab test reimbursement is not based on the Medicare Physician Fee Schedule Data Base, but on the Medicare lab fee schedule. Lab services have an RVU value of 0 in the MPFSDB.

Key points:
- Enroll in the program and obtain a CLIA license.
- Look at the updated lists of CLIA waived tests frequently.
- Perform the test in the approved manner.
- Assure that appropriate and timely quality control is being performed.
- Be sure that the test you are performing is being done using the method described in the CPT® book. For example, there are many ways to test glucose levels, so make sure that you select the CPT® code that corresponds with the method of testing you are using.
- Submit claims for CLIA waived tests to CMS with the QW modifier.

See also: Medicare Physician Fee Schedule Data Base.

Citations:

CMS, http://www.cms.hhs.gov/clia

Comprehensive Error Rate Testing (CERT)

Definition:

CMS's Comprehensive Error Rate Testing (CERT) program measures and reports the accuracy of paid Medicare claims.

Explanation:

According to CMS, each year the CERT contractor randomly selects 100,000 claims for review for each reporting period. This review assesses each claim for the accuracy of the provider coding as well as the accuracy of the Medicare carrier's claims processing. In addition, the CERT contractor assesses whether the claim complied with Medicare coverage, coding, and billing rules. The CERT contractor tracks the provider compliance error rate. CERT counts the following as errors:

1. Requests for which no documentation is received
2. Requests for which illegible or incomplete documentation is received
3. Errors in paid claims due to coverage, coding, or billing mistakes.

The CERT data also tracks carrier error rate, type of service error rate-labs, consults, etc.-and national paid claims error rate.

This data is available for download from the CERT website by Medicare Administrative Contractor and type of service.

Codes: All.

Coverage: Medicare.

Billing and coding rules:

If a physician office receives a request for medical record documentation for a specific service from the CERT contractor, the physician should carefully review the request and send the requested documentation. Sending this information is not a HIPAA violation. The practice does not need the beneficiary's signature to send the medical records, nor should the practice notify the beneficiary that the record was requested or sent.

The preferred method for submitting the data is via fax with a cover sheet that includes the bar code from the request. Even if mailed, the notes are scanned. If the legibility of the note is in question, faxing and scanning will certainly decrease its legibility. Be sure to send everything that relates to the service provided.

The patient name and another identifier should be on all pages sent. Sometimes the back page of a physician progress note in the office does not have the patient's name, so be sure to check for it.

If a provider fails to submit the requested documentation or if the claim was billed incorrectly, the provider will receive a request for a refund.

Respond to CERT requests promptly.

Related issues:

A CERT report provides important information about the error rate for each type of service paid by the carrier or fiscal intermediary. Although the claim volume for some services may be small for an individual carrier, in the aggregate, this is an excellent source of data. For example, established office visits have a significantly lower error rate than initial or subsequent hospital visits. Physician practices should review their own billing and coding and understand the coverage rules for services with a high error rate.

Key points:

- The CERT program measures the paid claims error rate nationally, by contractor, and by type of service.
- Physician overpayment errors will result in a request for a refund.
- Respond promptly to requests from the CERT contractor for medical record documentation. Sending medical records does not violate HIPAA regulations. A provider need not inform the beneficiary that a record was sent.
- Carriers will pay physicians who under-billed for services when these errors are discovered during CERT review.

See also: OIG work plan.

Citations:

CMS, http://www.cms.hhs.gov/CERT

CERT Provider web site, www.CERTprovider.org

Consolidated Nursing Home Billing

Definition:
Consolidated nursing home billing is a Medicare payment method that includes payment for some Part B services in the payments made to the skilled nursing facility (SNF) when the patient is in a covered Part A stay.

Explanation:
The Balanced Budget Act of 1997 requires Medicare to pay for services for patients in a Part A stay with a single payment to the SNF unless the services are specifically excluded from the inclusive payment. This includes payment for some services performed by physicians that would typically be paid on a fee for service basis by Part B.

During the Part A stay, if a physician provides a service, such as the technical component of a service that is included in the bundled prospective payment to the SNF, the physician must bill the SNF-and not Medicare or the patient-for that service (some exceptions apply). Other services performed by the physician or NPP after the Part A stay has ended must be billed to the SNF, and the SNF must look to the fiscal intermediary for payment.

Some medications are included in the SNF consolidated payment, and some may be billed separately.

These rules apply to patients in a Part A covered stay whether they are seen in the SNF, the physician office, or an outpatient department. That is, the rules apply to patients in a Part A covered SNF stay when seen at the SNF and in the physician office.

CMS updates the list of services included or excluded quarterly on its web site.

Codes: Vary by quarter.

Coverage: Medicare.

Billing and coding rules:
According to the CMS website, the following services are separately payable during a Part A covered stay:
- physician's professional services;
- certain dialysis-related services, including covered ambulance transportation to obtain the dialysis services;

- certain ambulance services, including ambulance services that transport the beneficiary to the SNF initially, ambulance services that transport the beneficiary from the SNF at the end of the stay (other than in situations involving transfer to another SNF), and roundtrip ambulance services furnished during the stay that transport the beneficiary offsite temporarily in order to receive dialysis, or to receive certain types of intensive or emergency outpatient hospital services;
- erythropoietin for certain dialysis patients;
- certain chemotherapy drugs;
- certain chemotherapy administration services;
- radioisotope services;

And

- customized prosthetic devices.

For Medicare beneficiaries in a non-covered stay, only therapy services are subject to consolidated billing. All other covered SNF services for these beneficiaries can be separately billed to and paid by the Medicare contractor.

Related issues:

Consolidated billing covers patients in a Part A covered stay. For patients in a Part B covered stay, only the physical and occupational therapy provisions apply. Practices need to know the status of the patient in order to know whether to bill place of service (POS) 31 (skilled nursing facility) or POS 32 (nursing home) when they bill for physician services. Services billed with POS 32 are reimbursed at a lower rate than services billed with POS 31.

Key points:

- The professional component (E/M services, diagnostic test interpretation) of physician services may be billed to Part B for patients in a covered Part A stay.
- These rules apply whether the physician provides the service in the SNF, in their own office, or in the outpatient department.
- Check the excluded/included list quarterly if you provide these services.

See also: Nursing facility visits.

Citations:

https://www.cms.gov/SNFConsolidatedBilling

Consultations

Definition:
An inpatient or outpatient consultation is a service provided by a physician or qualified NPP for the purpose of obtaining an opinion or advice regarding evaluation and treatment of a patient at the request of another physician or NPP. It is distinguished from another E/M service by the request for the opinion or evaluation, and requires that a report is returned to the requesting provider. If a transfer of care occurs, the service does not qualify as a consult, per CPT® in 2010. As of January 1, 2010, Medicare stopped recognizing the consultation codes. Commercial payers are free to recognize consult codes or follow Medicare's policy.

Explanation:
A consult requires a request for opinion from another health care provider. The request must be documented in the patient's medical records. After the consultant sees and evaluates the patient, a report must be returned to the requesting provider.

CMS stopped recognizing consults as of January 1, 2010, because they believed there was a high error rate in the use of these codes. Consultation codes have higher Relative Value Units, i.e., payment, than other E/M codes.

Codes:
99241–99245 for office, ED, observation and outpatient consults.
99251–99255 for inpatient and nursing facility consults.

Coverage:
Consultations are covered when medically necessary and the criteria for consultation are met. Fee-for-service Medicare no longer recognizes these codes, and many Medicare Advantage policies followed suit. More commercial payers have stop recognizing these codes over time.

Billing and coding rules:
The office and outpatient consult codes do not have new or established patient designations. A physician or NPP may bill a consult on a patient who is new or established to them, as long as the criteria for a consultation are met.

Who may request a consult? According to the CPT® definition, it may be another health care professional "or other appropriate source."

However, since most payers require the NPI number of the requesting provider on the claim form, the requesting provider for a consult is a health care professional who has a provider number and is able to bill third parties on their own. This means patients referred to the practice by a friend who is a nurse, by a physician referral service, or who come on their own are not consultations, but are new or established patient visits.

In 2010, CPT® added in the concept of transfer of care to the definition of consults. Previously, the concept of transfer of care was only a Medicare concept. However, CPT® included this in their definition in the CPT® book in 2010. CPT® does say, however, that if the purpose of the visit is to determine whether to accept the care of the patient, a consult may be billed. If the patient's care is transferred, a new or established patient visit should be billed, not consultation visits. A complete transfer of care occurs when the physician or NPP requests that another physician or NPP take over complete care of the patient for the condition and does not expect to continue caring for that patient for that condition. This transfer of care might occur between two physicians of the same specialty, when a patient is sent between sub specialists or if a patient moves from one city to another and the care is transferred to another physician. The difference is that the referring physician will not continue treating that patient for that problem, but is transferring care to the second physician.

How must the request for consultation come to the consultant's office? The request may be in writing or verbal between the two clinicians. For example, an internist sees a patient with persistent elbow pain. The internist has tried conservative treatment, such as medicine, physical therapy and home exercises but the patient continues to complain of pain. The internist sees the patient on May 5, 2010 and suggests that the patient be evaluated by an orthopedist for the problem. The medical record in the internist's office on that date of service should indicate the request for an orthopedic consult. When the patient is seen by the orthopedist, the orthopedist should indicate in the consult report that the patient is being seen at the request of Dr. Internist.

Consultants may initiate treatment or order tests and still bill for a consultation. After evaluating the patient, the consultant must send a report to the requesting provider.

A physician or NPP may request a consultation from another member of their own group if that provider has specific expertise required for the patient's care that is beyond his or her own expertise. CMS warns us that this should not be a routine request.

Consultations may be billed using time as the determining factor if more than 50% of the visit is spent in counseling, the nature of the counseling is described and the consultant documents the total time and that more than 50% of the total time was spent in counseling.

What codes should a physician use when billing a Medicare patient for a consult after 2010? In the office, bill a new or established patient visit. (Remember, a new problem does not indicate a new patient. A new patient is a patient who has never been seen by that physician, or another physician of the same specialty in the same group in the past three years.) If the patient is in observation status, use new or established patient visit codes (99201–99205). If the physician is called to the Emergency Department to perform a consult, use the Emergency Department codes, 99281–99285 for Medicare patients. CPT® instructs a physician to use the office and outpatient codes in that situation, but Medicare wants the ED codes.

If the patient is an inpatient in the hospital, bill for the consultation using the initial hospital services codes, 99221–99223, commonly described as admission codes. These initial hospital services codes are not defined as new or established, and may be billed by the consulting physician on new or established patients. The consultant bills these codes for the first visit and bills for follow up services with subsequent hospital visits. The admitting physician uses these same codes with an AI modifier, and that is how the payer distinguishes these services from the services of consulting physicians.

Related issues:

Practices must watch their payers' websites and newsletters to be sure that the payer still recognizes and pays for consultations.

Medicare as a secondary payer presents its own challenges. Options for office "consults":

- Bill primary with consult codes. Will cross electronically to Medicare and be denied. Resubmit electronically, with a note in *other information* field about primary payment. Requires handling of every claim. If primary allowance is more than Medicare, and small secondary Medicare balance may be okay.
- Bill primary with new or established patient visit code. Will cross electronically to Medicare and be paid automatically. Less revenue. No extra handling of claim.

Options for hospital "consults":
- Bill primary with consult codes. Will cross electronically to Medicare and be denied. Resubmit electronically, with a note in *other information* field about primary payment. May be best bet for hospital services.
- Bill primary with initial hospital services codes. How will they process multiple initial hospital services codes from different physicians?

Key points:
- Document the request for consultation in the patient's medical record. Many offices ask for a copy of the note for that date or ask the requesting provider to send you a written request for the consult.
- Document a verbal request in the consultation note (e.g., "I am seeing this patient at the request of Dr. Jones. In a phone conversation, he asked for my opinion about…").
- Document the written request ("I am seeing the patient at the written request of Dr. Jones for my evaluation of…").
- After performing the evaluation, send a report back to the requesting provider and keep a record that the report was returned.

See also: Shared visits, Incident to services, Time based codes.

Citations:

Medicare Claims Processing Manual, Pub 100-4, Chapter 12, Sections 30.6.10 and 30.6.11, http://www.cms.hhs.gov/Manuals/IOM/list.asp

CMS, Transmittal 782, Change Request 4215, released December 16, 2005.

CMS, *MLN Matters,* issue 4215, December 20, 2005.

Critical Care Services

Definition:

Critical care services are healthcare services provided to a critically ill patient and billed based on time documented in the medical record. The patient's condition must be critical, and the physician must be providing intensive medical services to the patient.

Explanation:

The *Medicare Claims Processing Manual* describes the service in Chapter 12, Section 30.6.12 A:

> Critical care includes the care of critically ill and unstable patients who require constant physician attention, whether the patient is in the course of a medical emergency or not. It involves decision making of high complexity to assess, manipulate, and support circulatory, respiratory, central nervous, metabolic, or other vital system function to prevent or treat single or multiple vital organ system failure. It often also requires extensive interpretation of multiple databases and the application of advanced technology to manage the critically ill patient.

Codes: 99291 and 99292.

Coverage: Most health insurance policies cover critical care services.

Billing and coding rules:

When billing for critical care services, the patient's condition must be critical as described in the paragraph above; the physician must be providing treatment for the patient's condition; and the time spent in providing the critical care must be documented in the patient's medical record. Although these patients are usually located in the intensive care unit, location is not the driving factor in billing for critical care. Patients who are receiving critical care may be on a medical surgical floor or in the ED. Conversely, simply because the patient is in the critical care unit does not mean that a physician can automatically bill for critical care.

The physician must be in attendance caring for the patient, meaning that the physician is on the unit, immediately available to the patient, and not caring for any other patient at that same time. The *Medicare Claims Processing Manual* describes this as "devoting his or her full attention" to the patient being treated. The physician may not include time spent on the phone directing the patient's care if he or she is off the unit during that time.

Time spent in critical care must be documented in the medical record. If time is not documented, the visit must be billed as a subsequent hospital visit. Physicians are paid much more for critical care than for subsequent hospital visits. Time is on your side, but only if you DOCUMENT IT for critical care. If the physician spends less than 30 minutes providing critical care service, bill the E/M service that is in the correct category (subsequent hospital visit, emergency department visit, etc.).

If a physician sees a patient multiple times on one date, add up the time spent during all visits per calendar date and bill that time. Physicians of the same specialty in a group should bill and be paid as if they were one physician. For critical care, this means the first doctor bills 99291, and all of the partners who see that patient and provide critical care on that date bill using 99292, the add-on code. More than one physician can not bill 99291 on the same date when the physicians are of the same specialty and in the same group.

Here is the chart from the *Medicare Claims Processing Manual* that shows how to use the codes, based on time spent providing critical care.

Total Duration of Critical Care	Code(s)
Less than 30 minutes	99232 or 99233
30–74 minutes	99291 x 1
75–104 minutes	99291 x 1 and 99292 x 1
105–134 minutes	99291 x 1 and 99292 x 2
135–164 minutes	99291 x 1 and 99292 x 3
165–194 minutes	99291 x 1 and 99292 x 4

Include time spent in the following services as part of critical care billing:
- Providing service at the patient's bedside
- Discussing the patient's condition with other physicians or other members of the patient's care team when on the unit and immediately available to the patient
- Reviewing data related to the patient

- Performing procedures that are bundled into the payment of critical care (listed below)
- Discussions with the family ONLY IF the discussion with the family involves obtaining clinically relevant history that the patient is unable to give or discussion with the family required because a family member must make medical decisions for the patient
- Writing notes in the chart

Do not include time spent in the following activities in your critical care time:

- Time off the unit, discussing the patient or giving orders by phone
- Discussions with the patient's family for the purpose of informing them about the patient's condition
- Performing procedures not bundled into critical care services
- Providing services to any other patients

The *Medicare Claims Processing Manual* specifically describes the need to document time:

> The duration of critical care time to be reported is the time the physician spent working on the critical care patient's case, whether that time was spent at the immediate bedside or elsewhere on the floor, but immediately available to the patient.

Certain services are bundled into the provision of critical care. Include the time spent in providing these services in the total critical care time, but do not bill these services in addition to critical care:

- Interpretation of cardiac output measurements (CPT® 93561, 93562)
- Obtaining chest X-rays (71010, 71015, 71020)
- Drawing blood for specimen (HCPCS G0001) (CPT® 36415)
- Reviewing stored data in computers (e.g. ECGs, blood pressures, blood gasses, hematologic data) (99090)
- Performing gastric intubation (91105, 43752)
- Performing pulse oximetry (94760, 94761 94762)
- Providing temporary transvenous pacing (92953)
- Managing ventilator settings (94002–94004, 94660, 94662)
- Doing peripheral vascular access procedures (36000, 36410, 36415, 36660)

If the physician performs other procedures, those may be billed separately. Do not include the time spent in performing non-bundled procedures into critical care time.

Can a physician be paid for another E/M service on the same day as critical care? Sometimes. The same physician may not be paid for both an ED visit and a critical care service on the same day. A physician can be paid for both an initial hospital service and a critical care service or a subsequent hospital visit and a critical care service if the documentation shows that the visits were **separate, distinct, medically necessary services**. Typically, the patient's status changes. For example, a physician may admit a patient in the morning to a medical unit. Later that day, the patient's condition worsens and the patient is moved to critical care. The physician may bill for both the initial hospital service and the critical care service as long as both are documented. (Remember, time must be documented in the medical record, not just the billing record, for critical care time.) Submit the bill with a 25 modifier on the initial hospital service, and send notes. A physician may bill for a subsequent hospital service and critical care, just as in the example above, if the patient's condition changes and both services are provided.

Medicare will only pay for critical care in the pre- or post-operative period in addition to the global fee if the critical care is unrelated to the surgery. The *Medicare Claims Processing Manual* gives this billing advice about billing for pre-operative critical care services:

> In order for these services to be paid, two reporting requirements must be met. Codes 99291/99292 **and** modifier 25 (significant, separately identifiable evaluation and management services by the same physician on the day of the procedure) must be used, and documentation that the critical care was unrelated to the specific anatomic injury or general surgical procedure performed must be submitted. An ICD-9-CM code in the range 800.0 through 959.9 (except 930–939), which clearly indicates that the critical care was unrelated to the surgery, is acceptable documentation.

The manual instructs us to append modifier 24 on critical care that was provided on the same day as a surgery but after the procedure was performed and only when the critical care was unrelated to the surgery. Only one physician may be paid for providing critical care at any one time. If two physicians are both attending to a patient in the same time period, only one may bill if the patient is a *Medicare* patient.

Other third party insurance companies may follow CPT® rules, which allows the physician to bill for complications of surgery.

Related issues:

Initial and subsequent hospital visits are per day codes. Critical care allows a physician to be paid for multiple episodes of care on a single day.

Key points:

- Document total critical care time per calendar date in the medical record.
- The patient must be critically ill and receiving treatment.
- Review the activities that can and cannot be counted in critical care time.

See also: Hospital discharge services, hospital initial services, hospital subsequent services, time based billing.

Citation:

CMS, *Medicare Claims Processing Manual*, Pub. 100–04, Chapter 12, Section 30.6.12, http://www.cms.hhs.gov/Manuals/IOM/list.asp

Days in Accounts Receivable

Definition:

This is a calculation of the number of days of gross charges that a practice has in accounts receivable outstanding. It is often called DRO for days in receivables outstanding.

Explanation:

This is an excellent measure of the practice's performance in collections. DRO should be monitored monthly and tracked for trends throughout the year. The number can vary in the short term due to high productivity in a month, low productivity, or high collections, but it serves as an important early warning measure for any problems.

Codes: Not applicable.

Coverage: Not applicable.

Billing and coding rules: Not applicable.

Related issues:

This is part of a monthly set of benchmarks to track how well a practice is managing its billing and collections. A significant increase in productivity one month can cause your days in accounts receivable to increase. Also, a significant increase in collection can cause a decrease in days in receivables.

DRO measures vary significantly by specialty. Norms may be available from specialty societies, and the Medical Group Management Association sells practice data.

Key points:

- Compare the practice's days in receivables with other practices of the same specialty.
- Practices with large worker's comp or third party liability claims will have higher days in receivables.
- The higher the percentage of payments at the time of service, the lower your days in receivables will be.

See also: Accounts receivable benchmarks, gross collection rate, net collection rate, aging of accounts receivable.

Citation:

Medical Group Management Association (www.mgma.com).

Practice Support Resources (www.practicesupport.com)

Diagnosis Coding

Definition:

The diagnosis code on the health insurance claim form tells the payer the diagnosis being treated, for the service that was performed, the reason for the service, or the signs and symptoms that led the patient to seek treatment.

Explanation:

For physician services, payers base their rates on the CPT® and HCPCS codes submitted on the claim form. The diagnosis code indicates the medical necessity for the service provided. While CPT® and HCPCS codes drive payment, the diagnosis code is often the reason for denial.

The documentation guidelines tell providers of healthcare services that each service requires an assessment:

The documentation of each patient encounter should include:

- reason for the encounter and relevant history, physical examination findings and prior diagnostic test results;
- assessment, clinical impression or diagnosis;

And

- The CPT® and ICD-9-CM codes reported on the health insurance claim form or billing statement should be supported by the documentation in the medical record.

Codes:

ICD-9-DM codes are listed in the ICD-9CM book and the Coding Clinic's quarterly update.

Coverage: All payers.

Billing and coding rules:

The explanatory material in the ICD-9 book provides specific rules for selecting a diagnosis code. These codes, adopted by all payers, are supplemented by payer rules that govern the ordering of codes and their use with certain diagnostic tests.

The ICD-9 book has two volumes; the first is a tabular list of diagnoses, and volume two is an alphabetical index. The user should look for a code in the index and then turn to the tabular list to select the most accurate and specific code. Never code from the alphabetic index.

In a physician note, diagnosis code information is written in the history as signs and symptoms, the reason for the visit, co-morbidities; and in the assessment. Code known diagnoses first. Code signs and symptoms if the diagnosis is not known. Each service provided should have a diagnosis code.

If a patient has a resolved problem and is being seen for surveillance, code the history diagnosis from the V10 through the V90 series of codes. For example, when seeing a patient at her 10-year check for breast cancer, bill with a surveillance code rather than the breast cancer diagnosis.

Transition to ICD-10:

The country is set to transition from ICD-9 to ICD-10 in October, 2013. ICD-10 is much more specific than ICD-9 and will require that physicians and NPP are more specific in their descriptions and assessments. The total number of available codes increases from about 13,000 to 68,000. CMS has provided a cross walk for about 75% of ICD-9 codes to ICD-10. CMS is holding provider calls to help educate physicians about the transition.

Coders will need more knowledge of diseases and anatomy to code with ICD-10. A good first step for many coders in preparation for ICD-10 is to take an anatomy and physiology course. As a next step, print out the top 25 diagnoses codes per physician, and look up the ICD-10 codes. Some diagnoses will need greater specificity in order to select a code. There are also free ICD-10 programs at www.codapedia.com.

Clinicians using EHR are selecting their own diagnosis codes. This is often a source of intense frustration because the terms they use to search are not always found in ICD-9 descriptions. One program that allows a graphical look up (reducing dependence on search terms) is medcodepix.com. It provides both ICD-9 and ICD-10 codes.

Related issues:

How many diagnostic codes should a physician or NPP include on a claim form? Physicians sometimes think that adding five, six, or ten diagnoses indicates the complexity of the patient. However, this actually causes confusion for the charge poster, who must select the diagnosis to enter into the first, second, and third positions. If a clinician indicates more than one diagnosis on the claim form, he or she should order the diagnoses and link them to the appropriate services.

Key points:

- Code for problems addressed at the current visit or service.
- Do not code past medical history or resolved problems when not addressed at that visit.
- If the diagnosis code is not known, code the signs and symptoms. However, once the diagnosis code is known, do not un-bundle the diagnosis into signs and symptoms. It would be incorrect to give the patient the diagnosis of fatigue when the provider knows that it is a symptom of that patient's depression.
- Do not code rule-out or probable diagnoses in physician office coding. It is incorrect to code rule-out lung cancer. If that is an unconfirmed diagnosis, code shortness of breath or coughing up blood for the reason for the visit.
- Code to the highest degree of specificity. Sometimes this includes a 4th or 5th digit.
- The ICD-9 code indicates certain codes which may not be used as primary diagnoses. Use these only in the secondary position.
- Code specific diagnoses when known in favor of non-specific diagnoses.
- Code the primary diagnosis first. You can code secondary tertiary or more diagnoses if addressed at that visit.

See also: Medical necessity.

Citations:

Introductory pages of ICD-9 book

CMS, *Medicare Claims Processing Manual*, Pub 100-04, Chapter 23;

http://www.cms.gov/Manuals/IOM/list.asp

www.medcodepix.com

www.cms.gov/ICD10

www.codapedia.com

Documentation Guidelines

Definition:
> The Documentation Guidelines are a set of guidelines jointly prepared by CMS and the American Medical Association (AMA) that describe principles of medical record documentation.

Explanation:
> The Documentation Guidelines serve as the basis of standards for E/M service documentation requirements. Good documentation is critical not only for high quality patient care, but to ensure that payers have the information necessary to validate each claim.
>
> These guidelines include general principles of medical documentation applicable to all medical services. The bulk of the guidelines provide the rules for selecting a level of E/M service. The 1995 and 1997 guidelines are currently in effect, and clinicians are permitted to use whichever set is more beneficial to them in documenting a service and selecting the level of service. The key components of E/M services are history, exam, and medical decision making.
>
> Clinicians generally prefer the 1995 guidelines, which have broader exam definitions. The 1997 guidelines allow clinicians to document the status of three chronic diseases as the history of the present illness (instead of the elements of the HPI), and had a much more specific multi-system exam. Auditors like this exam because it is less ambiguous than the 1995 exam. The 1997 guidelines also define a number of single specialty exams. These were especially helpful to psychiatry, ENT, and ophthalmology. Any clinician, not just specialists, may use these single organ system definitions.

Codes:
> All codes are covered by the general principles of the documentation guidelines. E/M services are specifically defined by these guidelines.

Coverage:
> Although these are Medicare implemented rules, they apply to all payers.

Billing and coding rules:
> The Documentation Guidelines work together with the CPT® book to define the level of documentation that is required for each level of service for an E/M code. That is, they define what level of history, exam,

and medical decision making are required for each level of service within each category.

The guidelines describe the documentation required for each of the four types of history: problem focused, expanded problem focused, detailed, and comprehensive. They define what is needed for each level of exam: problem focused, expanded problem focused, detailed, and comprehensive. In addition, the guidelines describe the criteria for the four levels of medical decision making: straightforward, low, moderate, and high.

However, in order to select a specific level of E/M code, providers and auditors must go back to the CPT® book, where the code descriptions include the level of history, exam, and medical decision making that are required. The CPT® book also tells you whether the code requires two or three of the three key components.

If time may be used as the determining factor to select the code, the times are listed in the CPT® book. There are some E/M codes for which time may not be used as the determining factor, including ED visits, and observation services.

The following very important instruction can be found in the section of the guidelines called "General Principles of Medical Record Documentation":

> The CPT® and ICD-9-CM codes reported on the health insurance claim form or billing statement should be supported by the documentation in the medical record.

Coders and billers have taken this to mean that if it wasn't documented, it wasn't done. In a more complex way, this informs clinicians that what they tell an insurance company was done must be supported in the medical record. It sounds simple, but it is a very important principle. Whatever procedure and diagnosis codes are reported on the claim form must be supported in the medical record documentation for that date of service.

Key points:
- All entries into the medical record must be legible.
- The Documentation Guidelines provide the basis of the requirements for selecting a level of E/M service.
- The guidelines also describe general principles of medical record documentation that are applicable to all services.

- The AMA and CMS developed these guidelines jointly.
- Physicians and NPPs may use whichever set of guidelines is more beneficial to the provider.

Related issues:

The Documentation Guidelines require that the legible identity of the provider should be noted in each entry into the medical record. The legible identity may be typed, dictated, or hand written. However, if only the signature of the provider is in the chart, make sure you have a signature log which indicates that that signature belongs to a specific provider. Medicare does not require that office notes be signed. This differs from a hospital, where there are many regulations that require signatures in addition to the legible identity of the provider.

See also: Legibility, general principles of medical record documentation, time based codes, E/M profiles.

Citations:

CMS, *Documentation Guidelines for Evaluation & Management Services*, http://www.cms.hhs.gov/MLNEdWebGuide/25_EMDOC.asp

CMS, *Medicare Claims Processing Manual*, Pub 100-04, Chapter 12, Section 30.6, http://www.cms.hhs.gov/Manuals/IOM/list.asp

Emergency Department Visits

Definition:

Emergency department visits are E/M services provided to patients in a facility that is open 24 hours a day for episodic non-scheduled care.

Explanation:

Emergency department services may be billed by physicians of any specialty, not just ED physicians. The physician does not need to be a regularly assigned physician in the ED in order to bill them.

Codes: 99281–99285

Coverage:

Most patients have coverage in their healthcare policies for emergency department visits. However, a payer may deny the service if the diagnosis that is submitted does not show that the patient needed emergency care. These are diagnosis related denials.

Billing and coding rules:

Most payers will pay for only a single Evaluation and Management (E/M) service per day per patient per physician. A physician who sees a patient in the emergency department, and later admits that patient to the hospital should bill for the initial hospital service only. The physician will not be paid for both an ED visit and a hospital admission on the same date. A physician also may not be paid for an ED visit and critical care on the same date. If a patient comes into the emergency room critically ill, bill only for the critical care time.

When a physician meets a patient in the ED to provide services on the weekend or after hours, and the location is selected for the convenience rather than for the necessity of ED services, bill outpatient codes 99201–99215.

An emergency department physician may ask the patient's own physician to see the patient in the ED. The ED physician is not asking for an opinion from the patient's own physician, but is typically asking for the physician to come in and take over care of the patient. The physician will decide whether to see the patient in the ED and send the patient home or admit the patient to the hospital.

According to the CPT® book, the amount of time spent with a patient does not affect the choice of the level of service for ED visits. That means that a physician may not use time as the determining factor in billing ED visits, and may not add prolonged services codes to the ED codes. However, a physician may bill for a procedure and an emergency department visit that are both medically necessary and are performed during the same visit. The E/M service—that is the ED visit—must meet the requirements of a distinct, separately identifiable service in order for a modifier 25 to be added.

Medicare pays physicians based on their group membership and on their specialty. So it is possible for the ED physician, the patient's own physician, and a specialist to all be paid for medically necessary emergency department services performed on the same day.

Related Issues:

Patients who are assigned to observation status and seen in the emergency department by a consultant should be billed using outpatient status as the place of service.

Key Points:

- Any physician or NPP may bill for emergency department visits when providing services in the emergency department.
- If a patient is admitted to the hospital from the ED, bill only for the initial hospital visit. Payers will not pay for both critical care and ED care billed by the same physician on the same date for the same patient.
- If the patient's personal physician is called to the emergency department by the ED doctor to provide a service, bill for that using either the emergency department codes 99281–99285 or the outpatient and office visit codes 99201–99215. Do not bill a consultation for these services, because consultation was not requested.

See also: Consultations, hospital initial services, critical care.

Citation:

CMS, *Medicare Claims Processing Manual*, Pub 100–04, Chapter 12, Section 30.6.11, http://www.cms.hhs.gov/Manuals/IOM/list.asp

E-Prescribing

Definition:

According to the CMS website, electronic prescribing (E-prescribing) is "a prescriber's ability to electronically send an accurate, error-free and understandable prescription directly to a pharmacy from the point-of-care" and it "is an important element in improving the quality of patient care." From a coding perspective, Medicare has initiated an incentive payment for physicians who use a qualified E-prescribing program for selected services and report on that use 25 times in a calendar year.

Explanation:

CMS is committed to value purchasing and increasing payment for quality—rather than the quantity—of services. The White House and CMS want physicians to use electronic health records and E-prescribing as a means of decreasing errors and improving quality. E-prescribing was part of the PQRI program, but was removed from that program and became a stand-alone incentive.

Codes:

Use Quality Data Codes when reporting with these CPT® codes:
99201-99215 for new and established patient visits
99304-99310, 99315, 99316 for nursing facility codes
99324-99328, 99334-99337 for domiciliary/rest home codes
99341-99345, 99347-99310 for home services
90801, 90802, 90804, 90805, 90806, 90807, 90808, 90809, 90862 for psychiatry codes
92002, 92004, 92012, 92014 for eye care codes
96150, 96151, 96152 for health and behavior assessment/intervention

HCPCS codes:
G0101 for screening pelvic and breast exam
G0108 for diabetes outpatient self-management training services, individual
G0109 for diabetes outpatient self-management training services, group

There is only one Quality Data Code to report for 2010, a change from the 2009 program. Check the CMS website to be sure that the code or the requirements did not change for 2011. For claims-based reporting, use this code in addition to the service listed above. Any diagnosis code is acceptable. For registry reporting, contact your registry for instructions.

G8553 for when at least one prescription created during the encounter was generated and transmitted electronically using a qualified eRx system

Coverage: Medicare

Billing and coding rules:

E-Prescribing starts as an incentive payment, but physicians who do not adopt a qualified E-prescribing program by 2012 will be penalized.

Incentive amounts:
  2009—2%
  2010—2%
  2001—1%
  2012—1%
  2013—.5%

Penalties for not reporting using a qualified e-prescribing system:
  2012—1%
  2013—1.5%
  2014 and each subsequent year—2%

There is no enrollment required to participate. Successful participation is measure by NPI, that is, by individual provider, not the group.

The program must be a qualified system. The system must perform these tasks:

- Generate a complete active medication list using electronic data received from applicable pharmacies and pharmacy benefit managers (PBM), if available
- Allows eligible professionals to select medications, print prescriptions and transmit prescriptions electronically and conducts all alerts. Alerts include automated prompts that offer information on the drug being prescribed and that warn the prescriber of possible undesirable or unsafe situations (e.g., potentially inappropriate dose or route of administration of the drug, drug-drug interactions, allergy concerns or warnings and/or cautions).
- Provides information on lower cost, therapeutically appropriate alternatives, if any. For 2009, a system that can receive tiered formulary

information, if available from the PBM would satisfy this requirement.
- Provides information on formulary or tiered formulary medications, patient eligibility and authorization requirements received electronically from the patient's drug plan (if available).

In addition, in order to be eligible for the incentive payments, 10% of the eligible professional's Part B charges must be comprised of the codes listed above.

The incentive is based on total Medicare allowable charges, billed to Part B for fee-for-service charges, excluding drugs and labs. Rural Health Centers and Federally Qualified Health Centers are not eligible because their claims are submitted to Part A.

Related issues:

E-Prescribing was a Physician Quality Reporting Initiative (PQRI) measure in 2008, but was given a separate incentive in 2009 and following years. PQRI is also funded in 2009 with a 2% incentive payment for successful reporting. The 2009 stimulus bill includes money for use of electronic health records.

Key Points:
- If a physician practice is not using an electronic health record and E-prescribing program, it is recommended to plan when and how to adopt those technologies.
- Use the e-Prescribing codes only with the office services listed above, not on any other codes or services.
- These services in the measure must be at least 10% of the provider's total Medicare charges.
- Report the G code at least 25 times in the calendar year with the appropriate code to be eligible.
- Any diagnosis is acceptable.
- Submit the quality data code with a $0 charge.

See also: PQRI

Citations:

http://www.cms.gov/ERXincentive/

http://www.ehealthinitiative.org

http://www.nationalerx.com/index.htm

https://www.cms.gov/eprescribing/

Evaluation and Management Services and Profiles

Definition:

Evaluation and Management (E/M) services are office visits, consults, hospital services, nursing home services, home services and preventive medicine services described in the first section of the CPT® book. The E/M profiles are normative data for the distribution of levels of service within each category of E/M code by specialty; they are commonly referred to as "bell curves."

Explanation:

E/M services account for a large percentage of all services billed by physicians of most specialties. Most of these codes can be broken down into three to five levels of service, with varying documentation requirements for the history, exam, and medical decision making required to meet the criteria for that level of service. Some also have typical time assigned. Physicians and qualified NPPs may use either the 1995 or the 1997 Documentation Guidelines select codes for these E/M services.

CMS publishes annual data describing the distribution of each level of service within each category of service, by specialty. Medicare carriers use this data to compare individual physician profiles to the norm, and physicians and NPPs run the risk of audit if their profile differs significantly from the norm for their specialty. NPPs are compared with nurse practitioners and physician assistants rather than by the specialty in which they work.

Codes: 99201–99350.

Coverage: All payers.

Billing and coding rules:

The requirements for billing E/M codes are based on two resources: the CPT® book and the Documentation Guidelines. Each code listed in the CPT® book describes the level of history, exam and medical decision making that is required for it, as well as whether two or three of the three key components are needed. The descriptions, however are defined by the Documentation Guidelines and not explained in the CPT® book.

Developed jointly by the AMA and CMS, CMS posts the Documentation Guidelines on its web site. Currently, providers may use whichever set of guidelines are more beneficial to them, the 1995 or the 1997 guidelines. The 1997 guidelines included single specialty exams that were more clinically appropriate for some specialists than the general multi-system exam. The good thing about these guidelines is that they have been around for so long that many clinicians understand them fairly well, and countless cheat sheets, tools, and templates are available to make documentation easier.

Carriers monitor the distribution of each clinician's E/M services by specialty and compare that with CMS norms. They do this within each category of service, such as established office visits, consults, subsequent hospital visits, etc. CMS publishes the raw data about code distribution by specialty on their web site, and many third party vendors package this and sell it in an easily usable format. If a carrier finds that a clinician's distribution of codes is significantly different than other providers of the same specialty, it is likely to trigger an audit of selected E/M codes.

Clinicians should not bill all of their services at one level in any one category. That is, do not bill all your admissions as level two admissions, all your subsequent hospital visits as level one visits, and all your consults as level four visits. CMS expects that the acuity of patients' presenting problems and the complexity of patients' conditions vary, so the level of service clinicians provide, document, and bill will also vary.

The CMS norms are not meant to be prescriptive. Physician practices will vary. But if a particular physician's profile differs significantly from the profiles of other physicians in the same specialty, it's prudent to ask why. Some physicians consistently bill codes at a low level out of confusion about the documentation guidelines and fear of an audit, while others routinely bill all high level services. Some clinicians bill all services within a category at the same level of visit. Any of these patterns increases the likelihood of audit.

Related issues:

In the introduction to E/M coding in the *Medicare Claims Processing Manual*, CMS says this about selecting a level of service:

> Medical necessity of a service is the overarching criterion for payment in addition to the individual requirements of a CPT® code. It would not be medically necessary or appropriate to bill a higher level of evaluation and management service when a lower level of service is warranted. The volume of documentation should not be the primary influence upon which a specific level of service is billed.

> Documentation should support the level of service reported. The service should be documented during, or as soon as practicable after it is provided in order to maintain an accurate medical record.

Use of an electronic medical record or paper template, often makes it easy to document a higher level of service. Keep in mind that the medical necessity for the level of service is the most important factor in code selection, not the volume of documentation. The ease of documenting higher levels of service with electronic tools does not justify billing high levels of service for problems with low or straightforward decision making.

Key points:

- Practices should compare each clinician's profile by specialty with the CMS norms once or twice a year.
- If a clinician has a significantly different distribution, take the time to find out why.
- Some physicians have practices that legitimately differ from the norm.
- Audit the clinician's E/M records for accuracy.
- Provide coding education and ongoing support.
- NPP data is collected by Medicare without regard to the specialty in which the NPP works. This makes comparisons more difficult, because the work and profile of a PA providing primary care services is certain to be much different from a PA working in oncology. Therefore, it is harder for practices to make realistic comparisons.
- A slight change in profiles results in a significant difference in revenue per office visit. If a practice finds significant undercoding, and through audits and education can change a provider's billing pattern, they can see revenue increases.

See also: Documentation Guidelines.

Citations:

CMS, Evaluation and management guidelines at http://www.cms.hhs.gov/MLNEdWebGuide/25_EMDOC.asp

CMS, *Medicare Claims Processing Manual*, Pub. 100-04, Chapter 12, Section 30.6.1, http://www.cms.hhs.gov/Manuals/IOM/list.asp

General Principles of Medical Record Documentation

Definition:

The first two pages of the Documentation Guidelines discuss general principles of documentation for all medical services.

Explanation:

These first pages explain the importance of documentation in the medical record. These principles relate to all medical and surgical services in all settings, not just E/M codes.

Codes: All codes are covered by these guidelines.

Coverage:

All payers follow the basic CPT® rules, ICD-9 rules, and the Documentation Guidelines in paying claims.

Billing and coding rules:

The Documentation Guidelines tell us that this documentation is important to ensure high quality care. The documentation for a medical service needs to be sufficient to be used by that provider, and by any other current or future providers who see the patient. It also allows for claims payments by accurately describing what was done at the medical encounter. Good documentation can be used for utilization review and quality control evaluation and for data collection that may be useful for research or education.

What do government and private payers want? Third party payers want accurate reporting of the procedure and the diagnosis codes that reflect the service provided. They also want to see the medical necessity for providing the service. As we know, medical necessity is required for payment of any service by third party payers.

When you look at the general principles of medical record documentation, one of the first requirements is that the record must be complete and legible. If only the physician and the practice staff can read the note, that is not considered a legible record. Other physicians and healthcare providers who would need to care for that patient should be able to be read it.

Related issues:

Medicare and most payers do not require a signature to pay for a claim, but they do require the legible identity of the provider to be included in the medical record. Practices governed by Joint Commission on Accreditation of Healthcare Organizations (Joint Commission) or rural health rules will have signature requirements. If the signature isn't legible, print, stamp or type the physician's name. Medicare has recently begun counting illegible signatures as errors.

Key points:

- Each patient encounter should include the reason for the patient's visit, relevant history and exam, and prior findings and diagnostic results. Each encounter should include an assessment or clinical impression or diagnosis. If the diagnosis is unknown, the patient's symptoms or complaints are documented as the clinical impression.
- The plan of care should be clearly written.
- The date and legible identity of the clinician should be documented.
- If tests are ordered, either the reason for those tests should be documented, or the reason for the test should be easily inferable.

See also: Legibility, Documentation Guidelines.

Citation:

CMS, Documentation Guidelines for Evaluation & Management Services, http://www.cms.hhs.gov/MLNEdWebGuide/25_EMDOC.asp

Global Surgical Package

Definition:

The global surgical package describes a set of services included in the payment for the surgical procedure.

Explanation:

Both the CPT® book and Medicare define the package of pre-operative, intra-operative, and post-operative services that are included in the global payment for a surgical service. Their definitions vary slightly, so physicians must use both when deciding what services are included in the global package (not separately billable) and what services are not included in the global package and may be billed and reimbursed separately.

Codes:

Surgical services with an indicator in field 16 of the MPFSDB that indicated a global period of 000, 010, 090, XXX or ZZZ.

Coverage:

Medicare definition for Medicare patients and CPT® definition for all other payers.

Billing and coding rules:

The surgical global period indicated in the MPFSDB indicates the number of follow up days included in the payment for the procedure. The end of the post-operative period is defined by these global days. Some minor surgical procedures and endoscopies have zero follow up days. Some minor surgical procedures have ten global days. Major surgical procedures have a 90-day global period. The global period starts the day of a minor procedure or the day before a major procedure. Physicians may be paid for the E/M service at which the decision to perform a major procedure was made. That is, a physician can bill for a consult, ED visit, office visit, hospital visit, or other E/M service which results in the decision for surgery that day or the next day. Medicare tells us to use modifier 57 for services with a 90-day global period and modifier 25 for services with a ten-day global period. This is not a CPT® definition.

Can a physician or NPP be paid for an E/M service and a minor surgical procedure on the same day? It depends. If a significant and medically necessary, separately identifiable service is provided, you can bill for it with an E/M service using the 25 modifier. The *Medicare Claims Processing Manual* gives us an example of this: a patient with a scalp laceration resulting from a fall must also have a neurological assessment. Another common example is when a pulmonary physician consults on a patient with a lung mass and decides to proceed to diagnostic bronchoscopy. Both of those services may be paid.

Typically, a physician who sees a new patient and performs a surgical procedure may bill for both the E/M service, and the minor surgical procedure. Both must be documented. It is less likely that the physician would bill for the E/M service for repeat scheduled procedures. However, both NCCI and the *Medicare Claims Processing Manual* say that the decision to perform a minor surgical procedure is included in the payment for the procedure and a separate E/M service is not payable. Compare these examples:

- A patient presents with a benign lesion and the physician destroys the lesion. Bill only for lesion destruction.
- A patient presents with abnormal uterine bleeding. After taking the history and performing the exam, the physician decides to do an endometrial biopsy. Bill both the E/M service and the procedure.

If a visit is scheduled for the purpose of performing a procedure, in general, bill only for the procedure.

The *Medicare Claims Processing Manual* describes those services that are included in and excluded from the global package:

Services included in the global package are:

- Pre-operative Visits—Pre-operative visits after the decision is made to operate beginning with the day before the day of surgery for major procedures and the day of surgery for minor procedures;
- Intra-operative Services—Intra-operative services that are normally a usual and necessary part of a surgical procedure;
- Complications Following Surgery—All additional medical or surgical services required of the surgeon during the post-operative period of the surgery because of complications which do not require additional trips to the operating room;
- Post-operative Visits—Follow up visits during the post-operative period of the surgery that are related to recovery from the surgery;
- Post-surgical Pain Management—By the surgeon;
- Supplies—Except for those identified as exclusions; and

- Miscellaneous Services—Items such as dressing changes; local incisional care; removal of operative pack; removal of cutaneous sutures and staples, lines, wires, tubes, drains, casts, and splints; insertion, irrigation and removal of urinary catheters, routine peripheral intravenous lines, nasogastric and rectal tubes; and changes and removal of tracheostomy tubes.

Medicare lists these services as excluded from the global package: Carriers do not include the services listed below in the payment amount for a procedure with the appropriate indicator in Field 16 of the MFSDB. These services may be paid for separately:

- The initial consultation or evaluation of the problem by the surgeon to determine the need for surgery. Please note that this policy only applies to major surgical procedures. The initial evaluation is always included in the allowance for a minor surgical procedure;
- Services of other physicians except where the surgeon and the other physician(s) agree on the transfer of care. This agreement may be in the form of a letter or an annotation in the discharge summary, hospital record, or ASC record;
- Visits unrelated to the diagnosis for which the surgical procedure is performed, unless the visits occur due to complications of the surgery;
- Treatment for the underlying condition or an added course of treatment which is not part of normal recovery from surgery;
- Diagnostic tests and procedures, including diagnostic radiological procedures;
- Clearly distinct surgical procedures during the post-operative period which are not re-operations or treatment for complications. (A new post-operative period begins with the subsequent procedure.) This includes procedures done in two or more parts for which the decision to stage the procedure is made prospectively or at the time of the first procedure. Examples of this are procedures to diagnose and treat epilepsy (codes 61533, 61534–61536, 61539, 61541, and 61543) which may be performed in succession within 90 days of each other;
- Treatment for post-operative complications which requires a return trip to the operating room (OR). An OR for this purpose is defined as a place of service specifically equipped and staffed for

the sole purpose of performing procedures. The term includes a cardiac catheterization suite, a laser suite, and an endoscopy suite. It does not include a patient's room, a minor treatment room, a recovery room, or an intensive care unit (unless the patient's condition was so critical there would be insufficient time for transportation to an OR);

- If a less extensive procedure fails, and a more extensive procedure is required, the second procedure is payable separately;
- For certain services performed in a physician's office, separate payment can no longer be made for a surgical tray (code A4550). This code is now a Status B and is no longer a separately payable service on or after January 1, 2002. However, splints and casting supplies are payable separately under the reasonable charge payment methodology;
- Immunosuppressive therapy for organ transplants; and
- Critical care services (codes 99291 and 99292) unrelated to the surgery where a seriously injured or burned patient is critically ill and requires constant attendance of the physician.

The surgeon may bill for an unrelated problem if the patient sees him for an E/M service. For example, an orthopedic surgeon who had operated on a patient's knee could see the patient during the global period for a shoulder problem. The surgeon would bill the E/M service with modifier 24 to indicate it was an unrelated problem in the global period.

However, if a return trip to the OR is required, bill for the second procedure with modifier 78. This does not restart the global period.

The CPT® definition of the global package includes normal follow ups. Complications of the global surgical period per CPT® rules may be billed with the 24 modifier. Medicare only pays for complications of surgery if a return trip to the OR is required.

Pre–operative medically necessary evaluations are separately payable from the global package, and these are discussed in more detail in the pre-operative entry in this book. Physicians who provide the entire global package—pre-operative, intra-operative and post-operative care—should use a surgical code without any modifier. Medicare pays for physicians in a group practice of the same specialty as if they were one physician. A covering physician who provides follow up care during the post-operative period is not paid separately. This coverage does not need to be indicated on the claim forms.

If a surgeon sees a patient and schedules the patient for surgery in 35 days, can the surgeon bill for a pre-operative history and physical? No. Although the hospital requires a history and physical, once the decision for surgery is made and the surgery is scheduled, do not bill subsequent E/M services. Sometimes, a patient receives part of the global service from one surgeon and part from another. This may occur when a patient needs emergency surgery when away from their home, but the post-operative care will be provided back in the patient's home city. In that case, bill the procedure with a 54 modifier for the surgical care only, and bill the same procedure code with a 55 modifier for the post-operative care. Both claims should use the same date of service and the same procedure code.

Physicians who follow up on minor surgical procedures performed in the ED may bill an E/M service code. The physician who performs a surgical service for a minor procedure in the ED may bill for that without a modifier.

A surgeon may indicate a staged related surgery during the post-operative period of a major surgery with modifier 58. This begins a new post-operative period. An unrelated second surgery by the same surgeon during a 90 day global post-operative period is billed using modifier 79 on the procedure code; this also begins a new post-operative period.

Related issues:
Medicare has set a policy which prohibits payment for an E/M service performed prior to a screening colonoscopy.

Indicators in the Medicare Physician Fee Schedule Data Base (MPFSDB) break out pre-op, intra-operative, and post-operative percentages for surgical package work. Other indicators also identify surgical add-on codes, codes which can be billed bilaterally, codes which can be billed with a surgical assist, and codes which can be billed with co-surgeons or team surgery. All surgical offices should print out or purchase a copy of this fee schedule annually.

Key points:
- The global period for a minor surgery begins the day of the procedure.
- The global period for a major surgery starts the day before a major procedure.
- Modifier use is critical to correct and accurate payment and reimbursement for surgical services.
- Payers will pay for medically necessary pre-operative visits performed by medical physicians.

- The visit at which the decision for surgery was made, if it is completed the day of or the day before the major surgical procedure, is billed with modifier 57.
- Consult the Medicare Physician Fee Schedule Database for important surgical indicators.

See also: Modifier 24, modifier 25, modifier 57, Medicare Physician Fee Schedule Data Base, pre-operative exams.

Citation:

CMS, *Medicare Claims Processing Manual*, Pub 100-04, Chapter 12, Section 40, http://www.cms.gov/Manuals/IOM/list.asp

Gross Collection Ratio

Definition:

The gross collection ratio tells a practice how much it collects for each dollar it bills. To determine the gross collection ratio, divide cash collections by gross charges.

Explanation:

Medical practices typically calculate the ratio on a monthly and year-to-date basis. Some practices calculate it on a rolling three to six month period. This calculation is affected by how high charges are set and by the level of reimbursement from major payers. The higher the charges, the lower the collection rate, and the lower the reimbursement from payers, the lower the collection rate will be.

Codes: All.

Coverage:

All. This calculation is relevant to your practice as a whole and to individual payers and types of service.

Billing and coding rules:

The gross collection ratio is not the best way of measuring practice efficacy in collections. Because it is influenced by the fee schedule and by payer allowances, it is a less accurate measure of collection efficiency. Gross collection rates vary considerably by area and specialty. It is most helpful to watch as a measure over time.

Related issues:

The net collection ratio and days in receivables provide better measures of the effectiveness of the billing staff.

Key points:

- Compare this calculation with the ratios of other practices of in the same specialty.
- This ratio is often particularly frustrating for doctors. Knowing that the practice collects only sixty cents on every dollar billed will often raise questions for physicians about how well the billing staff is doing. This is not the best measure of billing/collections performance.

See also: Account receivable benchmarks, adjusted collection ratio, days in accounts receivable, aging report.

Citation:

Normative data may be purchased from the Medical Group Management Association (www.mgma.com).

Practice Support Resources (www.practicesupport.com)

Healthcare Common Procedure Coding System (HCPCS)

Definition:

HCPCS codes are standard code sets used by health care providers and health insurance payers to report and pay claims.

Explanation:

HCPCS stands for Healthcare Common Procedure Coding System. Level one HCPCS codes are CPT® codes developed, maintained, and copyrighted by the American Medical Association. The level two codes are developed and maintained by CMS to describe services not defined by CPT® codes.

Codes:

There are over 10,000 HCPCS codes; these are found in the CPT® book and HCPCS book, both published annually.

Coverage:

All payers use these codes to process claims. Coverage for individual services described by these codes varies considerably by payer.

Billing and coding rules:

Both HCPCS level one and two codes provide a standard code set that describe medical services and procedures provided by physicians and other health care professionals. The AMA maintains level one CPT® codes and describes them in the CPT® book published annually, in their annual *CPT® Changes: An Insider's View,* and in the *CPT® Assistant,* a monthly newsletter.

Having a CPT® code associated with a service does not necessarily mean that that service is reimbursed by payers. CMS publishes an annual Medicare Physician Fee Schedule Data Base. (MPFSDB). In this data base CMS assigns both relative value units (RVUs) and billing indicators for each CPT® code. A code may be described by CPT®, have a status indicator of B (for bundled) in the Medicare database, and zero RVUs assigned. This tells you that this code is never billable to or payable by Medicare. Many private payers follow the bundling and status indicators and RVUs provided by CMS.

HCPCS codes are five digit, alpha-numeric codes that describe ambulance services, medicines, durable medical equipment, and some

services which Medicare covers and defines differently than CPT.®
CMS also uses HCPCS codes to differentiate between diagnostic and
screening services or to provide a distinction in coverage services.
CMS and the American Hospital Association joined together to be a
clearinghouse to answer HCPCS coding questions. They refer CPT®
questions to the AMA. In years past, there were level three codes, which
were local codes used by state Medicaid programs. With the advent of
HIPAA, these local codes are no longer in use.

Related issues:

Along with ICD-9 DM codes, HCPCS codes are the standard code sets
used by healthcare providers and payers.

Key points:

- Buy up-to-date versions of both the CPT® and HCPCS books each year.
- For medications listed in the HCPCS book, be careful about units.
  Depending on the medication, a practice may give one, two, or many
  units as a single dose.
- Supplies are described by HCPCS codes. Many supplies used in a
  physician office are not separately payable, but are bundled into the
  payment for the office visit or procedure. Medicare claims for durable
  medical equipment are processed by Durable Medical Equipment
  Regional Carriers (DMERC) contractors, not by carriers.
- Check with your private payers to see if they recognize services
  described by HCPCS codes.

See also: The Medicare Physician Fee Schedule Data Base (MPFSDB).

Citation:

CMS, http://www.cms.gov/MedHCPCSGenInfo

Hospital Discharge Services

Definition:

The services physicians provide on the final day of an inpatient admission are discharge services.

Explanation:

Physicians can bill for services provided to hospital inpatients on the final day of their stay using two CPT® codes, 99238 or 99239. These are time based codes and do not have specific requirements for history, exam, or medical decision making, as other E/M codes do. The physician must have a face-to-face service with the patient on the day of discharge to bill the discharge codes, but the physician is not required to examine the patient. These services can include any of the following: physically examining the patient, discussing the hospital stay and instructions for aftercare to the patient and/or caregivers, preparing discharge records or referral forms, and writing prescriptions.

Codes:

99238 Hospital discharge day management, 30 minutes or less
99239 Hospital discharge day management, more than 30 minutes

Coverage:

Most health insurance policies provide coverage for medically necessary hospital inpatient services.

Billing and coding rules:

Discharge visits require a face-to-face service with the patient. Only one physician may bill for discharge services. Other physicians or consultants who see the patient on the final day of a hospital stay should bill with subsequent hospital visit codes. If a physician sees the patient more than once on the day that the patient is discharged, only the discharge service is billable. Payers will not pay for both a subsequent hospital visit and a discharge visit on the same day, by the same physician or by physicians in a group of the same specialty.

The Internet Only Manual in the Teaching Physician Rules section (100.1.4) also instructs physicians that to use the two time based codes, time must be documented in the medical record for either level of discharge visit. In common practice, physicians rarely document time for the lower level discharge visit. However, in order to bill 99239 the total time of the discharge must be documented in the medical record.

Related issues:

Physicians can bill for a discharge visit on the same day as an admission to a skilled nursing facility. However, in order to bill for the admission to the skilled nursing facility, the physician must see the patient in the nursing home and document the level of service required for the admission. Do not rely on the same documentation for both hospital discharge and nursing facility admission. If both services are performed and documented, bill both. If only the discharge is performed and documented on that date, bill only for the discharge visit.

Key points:

- Document time in the discharge summary for code 99239.
- A physician must provide a face-to-face service on the date of discharge in order to bill for discharge services on that date.

See also: Hospital subsequent services, hospital initial services, inpatient, hospital observation services, time based billing

Citations:

CMS, *Medicare Claims Processing Manual*, Pub. 100-04, Chapter 1, Section 100.1.4 and Chapter 12, Section 30.6.9.2, http://www.cms.gov/Manuals/IOM/list.asp

Hospital Initial Services, Inpatient

Definition:

Commonly called the admission, the initial hospital care codes describe the first face-to-face encounter a physician has with a patient during an inpatient stay. Neither the word "admission" nor the phrase "history and physical" are descriptors in the CPT® book for this service.

Explanation:

The initial hospital service documents the reason for the admission; the symptoms or indications that led up to the admission; the patient's past medical, family, and social history; the examination of the patient; and the physician's assessment and plan. These services are per day codes. There are three levels of initial hospital services. For Medicare patients, starting January 1, 2010, the admitting physician adds an AI modifier to the initial hospital service.

Codes: 99221–99223.

Coverage: Covered by most payers.

Billing and coding rules:

Physicians should bill for the initial hospital service for the calendar date on which they have the first face-to-face service with the patient, even if that does not correspond with the date of admission to the hospital. For example, a patient is admitted to the hospital at 11:00 pm from the emergency department on November 11. The admitting physician comes into the hospital but does not have a face-to-face service with the patient until the next calendar day, November 12 at 1 am. The physician should bill for the initial hospital service on November 12. If the physician performs a subsequent hospital visit later in the day on November 12, the subsequent hospital visit will not be paid. All of the inpatient visit codes are per day, not per visit, codes. If the physician must see the patient more than once on the calendar date of the initial hospital service, only the initial hospital service is payable unless the patient is critically ill. Neither Medicare nor private insurance companies pay for multiple visits, as the description of the codes in the CPT® book as "per day" codes precludes this.

Only one physician can be paid for the initial hospital service for an inpatient admission. However, after January 1, 2010, consulting physicians who see Medicare inpatients will use the initial hospital services codes for the first visit in place of consultations.

When patients are admitted to the hospital by the same physician in the course of an ED visit or office visit, the physician can only bill for the initial hospital service. However, an ED physician can bill an ED visit on the same day that another physician bills for the initial hospital service.

In general, health plans pay for one E/M service per day, per physician in the same specialty of the same group. Two internal medicine doctors from the same group cannot both be paid for hospital services to a single patient on a particular day. However, an internal medicine doctor and a cardiologist can both be paid for providing medically necessary services on the same patient, even if they are in the same group.

A Medicare transmittal instructed physicians about how to bill the initial service if they see a patient in their office, bill a level five consult or office visit, and then admit the patient in the next several days. In that case, carriers are instructed to pay the level five visit as billed, but pay the admission as a level one initial care service. Medicare assumes that the work for these services would overlap, and they do not want to pay twice for the same work.

What if a physician admits and discharges a patient from inpatient status on the same calendar date? A series of codes (99234–99236) describes this service, admission, and discharge to observation or inpatient status on the same calendar date.

Whether a physician can bill for critical care and an initial hospital service on the same day depends on the situation. In general, remember that Medicare does not pay twice for the same work. If a physician admits a patient in the morning who is not critically ill, and the patient becomes critically ill later in the day, requiring a transfer to the ICU, bill for the admission in the morning and the critical care in the afternoon. However, if the patient was critical at the time of admission, bill only for the critical care time. See the section on critical care for more detail.

Initial hospital services have typical times listed for them in the CPT® book. Bill these services based on the total time spent on the unit doing the admission, if more than 50% of the time was spent in counseling and coordination of care.

Related issues:

Physicians should document for initial hospital services carefully. Although the patient's condition may warrant a level two or level three initial service, the documentation often lacks a comprehensive history or a comprehensive exam. A level two or three admission requires a comprehensive history: four history of the present illness items, 10–14 systems reviewed in the review of systems, and all three of past medical, family and social history. Many admissions lack a complete review of systems and family history, and thus audit at the lowest level of admission. Also, level two and level three admissions require a comprehensive exam. For many physicians, this is an eight organ system exam as described in the 1995 set of guidelines. Refer to the Documentation Guidelines for more information.

Key points:

- A physician should bill for the admission on the calendar date of the first face-to-face service with the patient in the hospital.
- In addition to the chief complaint and HPI, document a complete review of systems, all of past medical, family and social history, and an eight-organ system exam for all admissions. Then, select your level of service based on the medical decision making-that is, how sick the patient is upon admission.

See also: Hospital discharge services, hospital subsequent services, hospital observation services, critical care, time-based billing

Citations:

CMS, *Medicare Claims Processing Manual*, Pub. 100-04 Chapter 12, Section 30.6.9, http://www.cms.gov/Manuals/IOM/list.asp

CMS, http://www.cms.gov/MLNEdWebGuide/25_EMDOC.asp

Hospital Observation Services

Definition:

These are services provided to patients who are designated as "observation status" at a hospital.

Explanation:

There are times when a physician wishes to observe a patient in the hospital and expects the patient to go home within a short period of time. Instead of admitting the patient to inpatient status, the physician admits the patient to observation status. The patient may physically be in the emergency department, in a designated observation unit, or in a bed that is more typically used for inpatient status. The location of the patient does not determine the status; the status is designated by the physician at the time of the patient's admission.

Codes: 99218–99220, 99217, 99234–99236.

Coverage:

Third parties and Medicare typically pay for observation services. Whether hospitals can bill separately for an observation admission depends on the patient's diagnosis for Medicare. This means that the financial incentives for physicians differ from those for a hospital.

Billing and coding rules:

If a patient is admitted to observation status in the course of an office visit or ED visit, the admitting physician should bill only for the initial observation services, 99218–99220. The physician should note the date and time of the observation admission. All other physicians who see the patient while in observation status should bill using office/outpatient visit codes or outpatient consultation codes. For Medicare patients, consulting physicians should report office/outpatient codes, 99201–99215. For commercially insured patients, use outpatient consult codes 99241–99245. Time may not be used as a factor when selecting an observation code status, and prolonged service codes may not be added to observation visit codes.

Observation billing raises a number of "what if" questions. Here are some common examples of observation billing (see next page).

Example 1	Bill with these series of codes
Patient admitted to observation status (OBS), April 1, 9:30 pm	99218–99220
Patient remains in OBS status, April 2	99212–99215
Patient discharged, April 3	99217

In this example, the patient remains in observation status for part of three calendar days. This is not typical but happens from time to time. Bill the first day using initial observation status codes; bill the second day with outpatient/office visit codes, because the patient is not an inpatient. Bill the final day using the observation discharge code. This is a CMS, not a CPT® rule. CPT® recommends billing the second day of an observation admission with the unlisted E/M code 99499. Most practices use and payers pay for an office visit code on the second day.

Example 2	Bill with these series of codes
Patient admitted to observation status, April 1, noon	
Patient changed to inpatient status, April 1, 5 pm	99221–99223

In example two, the patient is admitted to observation status, but the physician changes the patient status to inpatient on the same calendar date. Bill only for the initial inpatient service, not for the initial observation service.

Example 3	Bill with these series of codes
Patient admitted to observation status, April 1, 8 am	
Patient discharged to home, April 1, 5 pm	99234–99236

The CPT® definition of these codes is for admission and discharge on the same day to observation or inpatient status. They have higher

RVUs than the other initial hospital service codes, because the work for the discharge is included in them. In order to bill these codes, the patient must be admitted and discharged on the same calendar date. Medicare has an additional rule: the patient must be in observation status for over eight hours in order to use these codes. Also, the physician must see the patient twice and separately document the admission and discharge.

Hospital and physician status billing:

The status of codes reported (i.e., billed) by the physician should match the status reported by the hospital. If the hospital changes the admission status from observation to inpatient status, the physician coding should match. If not, the claim is often denied by the payer. Physician practices may not know that the hospital status changed until they receive a denial from the payer.

Related issues:

The relative value units and payments for initial hospital services and observation services are almost the same. The documentation requirements for these initial observation services are identical to the documentation requirements for initial hospital services. Physicians should remember to document a complete review of systems and past medical, family and social history. Without all three elements of the patient's history, the initial observation service will audit at the lowest level. The place of service for observation service is 22, outpatient.

Hospitals only receive separate payment from Medicare for observation services for patients with three diagnosis codes. However, observation status begins and ends with the physician. That is, it is the physician who designates the status of the patient in the hospital.

Key points:

- Select observation codes based on the status of the patient in the hospital.
- Note the time of the admission to observation status.
- If a patient remains in observation status on the second calendar date, bill using office/outpatient codes, not subsequent hospital visits.
- When the patient status is changed to inpatient status, bill subsequent hospital visits.
- If a patient status is changed from observation to inpatient on the same date that the patient was admitted to observation, bill only the inpatient initial service.

- For non-Medicare patients, bill consults based on the status of the patient. Bill outpatient consults for patients in observation status and bill inpatient consults for patients who are inpatients.
- Use the observation discharge code to report discharging a patient from observation services, but do not bill for the discharge from observation and the admission to inpatient status on the same day.

See also: Hospital subsequent services, hospital initial services, hospital discharge services, time based billing

Citation:

CMS, *Medicare Claims Processing Manual*, Pub. 100-04, Chapter 12, Section 30.6.8, http://www.cms.gov/Manuals/IOM/list.asp

Hospital Subsequent Services

Definition:

Subsequent hospital services refer to care provided by the attending physician to a hospital inpatient. Consulting physicians providing care to an inpatient after an initial consultation also use the subsequent hospital services code.

Explanation:

Commonly referred to as "daily rounds," subsequent hospital services include all of the daily care provided by the attending physician, including medical record review, history taking and examination of the patient, review of diagnostic results from the previous day, record keeping, and development of the assessment and discharge plan. The service also includes discussions with the hospital staff, other physicians, the patient, and the patient's family. The definition of the visits is per day, so only bill one unit per day of the subsequent hospital visit codes, no matter how many times the physician saw the patient that day.

Codes: 99231–99233.

Coverage:

Most health insurance policies provide coverage for medically necessary hospital inpatient services.

Billing and coding rules:

These are per day, not per visit codes, so bill only once for a patient's care on a single calendar date no matter how many times the physician saw the patient that day. What if the physician is called back to the hospital later in the day? A physician can add the documentation for two visits to determine the level of service, and if documented, bill a higher level. But only one visit is payable. Likewise, if the physician's partner is covering for the attending physician, and the two physicians are of the same specialty, only one visit is payable for that date.

Multiple physicians of different specialties can bill for medically necessary hospital visits. That is, an internist, a cardiologist and a renal specialist may all bill and be paid for subsequent hospital visits on the same date if they are providing medically necessary services. Although different diagnoses will decrease the likelihood of an initial denial and need for appeal, they are not required.

However, only one physician may bill a discharge visit; other physicians of different specialties who provide medically necessary hospital services on the day of discharge should bill a subsequent hospital visit. A physician can not bill both a subsequent hospital service and a discharge visit on the same day.

Subsequent hospital visits have typical times associated with them in the CPT® book, so a clinician may use time to select a subsequent hospital visit if more than 50% of the visit is spent in discussion/counseling with the patient.

Bill for the calendar date that the physician saw the patient for subsequent hospital visits. If the patient was admitted on January 1 at midnight, and the physician had a face-to-face service with the patient at 2:00 a.m. and performed the initial hospital service (commonly called the admission), the physician will not be paid for a subsequent hospital visit at 10:00 a.m. on the same calendar date. Only one E/M service is payable per date for physicians of the same specialty in the same group, and additional subsequent hospital visits will not be paid.

Related issues:

Medicare has a third party contractor conduct reviews of paid claims—Comprehensive Error Rate Testing (CERT)—to see if payment made by carriers to physicians is accurate. CMS finds that the documentation needed to support the highest level of subsequent hospital visit is frequently missing when they review the record. Two of the three key components of history, exam, and medical decision making are required. The required history is four elements of the history of the present illness, with two to nine systems reviewed; the exam 12 elements examined, using the 1997 guidelines; and the medical decision making is high complexity.

Key points:

- Bill only one subsequent visit per calendar date.
- Be careful about handwriting, because the documentation must be legible in order for the visit to be payable.
- Document a history of the present illness by describing the patient's symptoms or illness during the past 24 hours. "Patient sitting in bed," does not qualify as a history.

See also: Hospital discharge services, hospital initial services, hospital observation services, critical care, time based billing

Citation:

CMS, *Medicare Claims Processing Manual*, Pub. 100-04, Chapter 12, Section 30.6.9, http://www.cms.gov/Manuals/IOM/list.asp

Immunization Administration for Vaccinations

Definition:

The CPT® book describes eight codes for the administration of vaccinations. CMS defines additional codes for administration of immunizations that are covered by Medicare as preventive medicine services.

Explanation:

Vaccine administration is separately payable from the vaccine serum itself. For some patients and some vaccines, the state provides the vaccine to the medical practice free of charge. However, states have developed guidelines with age and frequency limits for the free provision of vaccinations. Some vaccines are never provided by the state, such as those related to travel to a foreign country. When a practice receives the vaccine at no charge, it bills for only the vaccine administration. The practice bills for the vaccine administration and for the vaccine itself if it has paid for the vaccine.

These charges are in addition to the preventive medicine services, which are billed separately. There are eight CPT® codes that describe this service, including base and add-on codes.

Codes:

90465 through 90474. CMS also developed HCPCS codes for administration of covered preventive medicine services. These are G0008 for the influenza administration, G0009 for pneumococcal administration, and G0010 for hepatitis B administration. CMS developed G9141 for administering the H1N1 vaccine.

Coverage: Varies, and can be diagnoses dependent.

Billing and coding rules:

Bill for the vaccine administration when the office administers the vaccine. Bill for the vaccination toxoid if the practice paid for the product.

The codes 90465 and 90466 are used to bill for the administration of a vaccine to patients under the age of eight, with physician counseling. Code 90465 is for the first administration, including percutaneous, intradermal, subcutaneous, or intramuscular injection, when the provider who administers the vaccine also counsels the patient. Nursing or staff counseling is not sufficient to bill this code. Code 90466 is for each additional administration provided on the same day by the same means. This is an add-on code and would never be billed separately from the base code 90465. Bill the number of additional units of service provided. For example, if a physician provided three intramuscular vaccines in a patient under the age of eight with counseling, bill 90465 with one unit, and 90466 with two units.

Vaccine administration with provider counseling for patients under the age of eight is billed using code 90467 for the first administration via percutaneous, intradermal, subcutaneous, or intramuscular injection. Code 90468 is for each additional administration. Codes 90471 and 90472 are for the administration for patients who are older than eight years old. Codes 90473 and 90474 are used for administration of vaccines by intranasal or oral route. Again, these are defined as the base codes and the add-on codes.

Related issue:

CMS has developed HCPCS codes for administration of covered preventive vaccinations. These are typically diagnosis specific.

Key points:

- Select vaccine administration based on the age of the patient, method of administration, and whether or not counseling is provided by the clinician.
- There are a series of add-on codes for additional units. Add-on codes can never be billed alone; they must always be billed with the base code. They are defined as each additional code, so bill these codes with a number of units.
- For Medicare preventive medicine services, bill the appropriate HCPCS codes and related covered diagnoses.
- Report only one initial administration code per claim.
- Do not report a nurse visit for a patient who presents for the administration of a vaccine. Report the correct administration code.

See also: Preventive medicine, preventive medicine services for Medicare patients.

Citation:

CDC, http://www.cdc.gov/nip/menus/vaccines.htm_Schedules

Incident to Services (Medicare)

Definition:

Medicare defines incident to services as services provided in a physician office to Medicare patients that are incident to a physician's treatment and plan of care.

Explanation:

Incident to services are provided in a physician office and billed as if they were personally performed by the physician. The claim is submitted using the physician's provider number and is paid at 100% of the physician fee schedule. Two common services are billed in the office as incident to. The first is a nurse visit, which may only be billed at the 99211 level. The second is for the services of a qualified NPP, and those may be billed at the level of services provided to an established patient visit. In order for the practice to bill a service as incident to, the physician must have seen the patient first for that problem and established a plan of care. NPPs must bill new patients under their own provider numbers. Only follow up care that was initiated by a physician may be billed as incident to if the following criteria are met:

- The staff member providing the service is employed by the physician or the group that employs the physician. Leased and contracted employees are permitted.
- The physician who initiated the plan of care is in the office and immediately available to provide assistance. The physician's partner may serve this function in a group practice.
- The service being provided is follow up care. Because the care is incident to, no new patients and no new problems on established patients may be billed this way.
- The service is provided in the office, not the hospital, outpatient department, or nursing home. It must be an expense to the physician.
- The physician that initiated the plan of treatment remains actively involved in the plan of care. The physician and NPP may alternate seeing the patient.

An NPP can see new patients and treat established patients for new problems, but the NPP must bill these services under his or her own provider number (not incident to the physician) and be paid at 85% of the physician fee schedule amount.

Codes:

E/M codes. A physician does not need to be in the office to bill flu shots, EKGs, lab services, or x-ray services, because these are covered under a different statute and do not count as incident to services.

Coverage:

Incident to is a Medicare rule. State Medicaid programs often follow incident to rules. Check with other third party payers about their rules for billing NPPs and nurse visits.

Billing and coding rules:

To bill a service incident to the physician service and be paid at 100% of the physician fee schedule, the service must be an integral part of the physician treatment. This means that the physician must see the patient for that problem first and establish a plan of care. The physician also must stay involved in the patient's treatment and must be physically in the office at the time the service is performed, immediately available to provide assistance. Some practices alternate visits between a physician and NPP. If the physician is in the car, at the hospital or on vacation, bill the service as incident to using the NPPs provider number. However, if another, supervising physician in a group practice is available and in the office, the practice may bill the service as incident to.

The employee providing the service must be an expense to the practice: an employee of the physician, an employee of the group that employs the physician, or a leased or contracted employee.

Incident to services provided in the patient's home are payable IF both the physician and the employee are present when the services are provided. These situations are rare. For all practical purposes, incident to services are billed and payable in the physician office.

New patient visits may never be billed as incident to, because they do not meet the definition of being part of the physician's plan of care. These services may be billed by NPPs under their own provider numbers.

Related issues:

Some practices bill all of their NPP services under the practice's provider number, losing the 15% reimbursement difference just for ease of billing and uncertainty about the rules. Practices that want to collect the revenue difference need to educate their NPPs about the rules for incident to services, and ask the NPP to indicate on the encounter form whether the service is an incident to service or a direct bill service. Because this is the source of so much confusion, educate the providers and staff annually about it. Incident to represents both a compliance risk and a potential revenue issue.

Key points:
- Incident to services are services billed to Medicare as if the service was provided by the physician.
- Incident to services may be billed in the physician office but not in the hospital or nursing home for Medicare patients.
- Incident to services are paid at 100% of the fee schedule.
- The physician must initiate the care, stay actively involved, and be in the office immediately available when the service is provided.
- The staff member providing the service must be an expense to the practice.
- Do not bill new problems or new patients as incident to.

See also: Nurse visits, shared visits.

Citations:

CMS, *Medicare Benefit Policy Manual*, Pub 100-02, Chapter 15, Sections 60.1, 60.2, and 60.3, and CMS, *Medicare Claims Processing Manual*, Pub 100-04, 02, Chapter 12, Section 30.6.4, http://www.cms.gov/Manuals/IOM/list.asp.

Legibility

Definition:

All medical records must be complete and able to be read by other providers.

Explanation:

The Documentation Guidelines, a joint effort of CMS and the AMA, require that all medical records be legible. Medical records are used by many more people than just the healthcare provider who prepares the note. Medical records are intended to be used by that provider over time, and by other healthcare providers who may participate in the care of the patient.

Medical records also serve as a basis for claims, so a payer that has questions about a claim that was submitted to them uses the medical record to verify the service that was billed was actually the service that was provided. Medical records are also used for quality control and for utilization review purposes. In order to use them for all these important purposes, the medical record must be legible.

Codes: All codes in the CPT® book.

Coverage:

Medicare and third party payers require legibility in order to pay for a medical service.

Billing and coding rules:

Medical records must be complete and legible. Ample evidence suggests that illegible handwriting leads to errors in medications and other treatments.

How can you judge if a medical record is illegible? One test is to ask healthcare providers to read their writing back to themselves. If they cannot read their own writing a week or a month after they have written it, the record is usually considered to be illegible.

Another test is to give the record to a healthcare provider who will need to carry out the orders written by the clinician. If the healthcare professional who needs to carry out the orders is unable to read them, the orders are considered illegible.

Some payers will have two reviewers try to read the note, and if neither of them is able to decipher the note, the record is considered illegible.

In general, an auditor or other healthcare professional should be able to scan along and read the note at a normal pace. There may be a word here or there that can't be read, but if most of the note is legible and can be read at a normal pace, consider that a legible record. If the reader must work to decipher each word, word by word, that record may be considered illegible. No healthcare provider receiving that record on a patient who has transferred care will have the time and patience to look at the record word by word.

Providers can address legibility problems by using voice activated software, electronic medical records, forms with templates, or dictation. If a provider is hand writing a note and has a question about its legibility, the provider may ask a staff member to read it. If a practice has clinicians with illegible handwriting, it should implement electronic prescribing methods.

Related issues:

Many practices use electronic medical records or templates to help decrease the burden on practitioners and increase the legibility and usefulness of their records. These are good alternatives for providers whose writing is not consistently readable.

Key points:

- All entries into the medical record must be legible.
- Use voice activated software, dictation, electronic health records or templates to help a provider with difficult to read handwriting.
- Practices and hospitals should use all means available in their governance rules to prevent a clinician whose handwriting is illegible from continuing to practice and document in that manner.

See also: Documentation guidelines, general principles of documentation.

Citation:

CMS, www.cms.gov/MLNEdWebGuide/25_EMDOC.asp.

Local Coverage Determinations (LCDs)

Definition:

Local Coverage Determinations are contractor specific rules developed in the absence of national coverage or coding policies, or as an adjunct to national coverage. LCDs were mandated in 2003 to replace Local Medical Review Policies.

Explanation:

CMS developed National Coverage Determinations (NCDs), which define coverage policies for medical services. These NCDs define when Medicare will cover a service based on the patient's condition, symptoms, or diagnosis codes. NCDs apply to all carriers and localities throughout the country. In the absence of a national policy, local Medicare Administrative Contractors (MACs) may develop their own policies, provided they are in compliance with national coverage and coding rules.

Codes: As selected by the MAC.

Coverage:

These are Medicare policies, but many private policies base their coverage decisions on these policies.

Billing and coding rules:

LCDs provide guidance to the physician practice about whether a service is considered reasonable and necessary for a patient's condition, and when and at what frequency the service will be covered. These LCDs must comply with national coverage and coding rules, and they are secondary to national policies.

CMS's web site includes a searchable database of LCDs.

Each LCD provides general information, the contractor name, the effective and revised dates, a description of the CMS national coverage policy, and the geographic locale to which the policy applies. LCDs also list the range of codes, a description of the service, indications and limitations of coverage and/or medical necessity, specific CPT® codes, ICD9 codes, coding guidelines, documentation requirements, and utilization guidelines.

Related issues:

NCDs and LCDs address the issue of medical necessity. If a physician recommends a lab test or medical service to a patient who does not meet the criteria for the service based on the LCD or NCD, and the physician and patient wish to proceed, the physician should obtain an Advance Beneficiary Notice (ABN) prior to proceeding. This allows the physician to hold the patient financially responsible for the service.

LCDs and NCDs provide the physician practice with specific guidance about whether a service is covered and payable. Physicians may disagree with the medical necessity as defined by the policy, but the policy is specific and gives them the billing guidance they need.

Key points:
- Physicians should check their contractor's web site for LCDs for services they provide.
- Review the covered indications for the service.
- Develop a procedure to inform patients prior to providing the service when the service is not covered for their condition.
- Execute an ABN properly.

See also: National Coverage Determinations, Advance Beneficiary Notice

Citations:

CMS, http://www.cms.gov/DeterminationProcess

CMS alphabetical NCD listing: http://www.cms.gov/mcd/index_list.asp?list_type=ncd

CMS, Medicare coverage searchable data base: http://www.cms.gov/mcd/search.asp?

Locum Tenens Billing

Definition:

Medicare allows a physician to bill for services provided by a substitute physician under a locum tenens arrangement when the regular physician is away.

Explanation:

A physician who is absent from the practice due to illness, vacation, pregnancy, or continuing medical education may elect to hire a temporary physician on a per diem basis or a fee-for-time basis. This substitute arrangement, which may continue for a maximum of 60 continuous days, is paid by Medicare following the rules for locum tenens billing.

Codes:

Modifier Q6 is appended to the procedure code on the CMS 1500 form.

Coverage:

This is a Medicare rule. Check with your third party payers before using a locum tenens arrangement for their patients.

Billing and coding rules:

Physicians who are away from their practices may bill for the services of a locum tenens physician using their own provider number. The regular physician must be unavailable to provide care, typically due to an extended illness or a vacation, and the Medicare beneficiary must seek medical care. The regular physician pays the locum tenens physician on a per diem or a fee-for-time basis. The maximum period for this coverage is 60 continuous days. Once the first coverage day has occurred, days in which the locum tenens physician may not provide any service count toward this time period. When the regular physician submits the claim, append modifier Q6 to the procedure code in item 24D of the CMS 1500. When using the updated CMS 1500 form (effective October 2006), practices will be required to list the provider identification number of the locum tenens physician on the claim form. The regular physician is required to keep a record of the patients seen by the locum tenens physician and billed using the Q6 modifier.

Providers may not bill for an NPP using a locum tenens arrangement.

Related issues:

Post-operative care provided by a locum tenens physician as part of the global surgical period does not need to be identified on the claims form. A locum tenens physician may also be hired by a group practice to provide services when a physician has left the group. The group may bill for the locum tenens services for a maximum of 60 days using the provider number of the physician who has left the group.

Key points:

- The practice bills for the services of the locum tenens physician under the regular physician's provider number when the regular physician is unavailable and the Medicare patient seeks care.
- Pay the locum tenens physician on a per diem or fee-for-time basis.
- The maximum time period for this billing arrangement is 60 days.
- Append a Q6 modifier to the procedure code when submitting the claim to Medicare.
- Keep a record of the patients seen by the locum tenens physician.

See also: Reciprocal billing

Citation:

CMS, *Medicare Claims Processing Manual*, Pub 100-04 Chapter 1, Section 30.2.11, http://www.cms.gov/Manuals/IOM/list.asp

Medical Necessity

Definition:

Medically necessary healthcare services are those services that would be provided by a prudent physician to evaluate, diagnose, or treat an illness, injury, disease, or symptoms. The definition of what is medically necessary can be straightforward or slippery, depending on one's perspective.

Explanation:

All claims for medical services to Medicare and other third party payers must be medically necessary in order for the claim to be paid. Healthcare providers indicate medical necessity by the diagnosis code on a claim form.

Codes: All.

Coverage: All.

Billing and coding rules:

The Medicare web site glossary defines medical necessity for beneficiaries this way:

> Services or supplies that: are proper and needed for the diagnosis or treatment of your medical condition, are provided for the diagnosis, direct care, and treatment of your medical condition, meet the standards of good medical practice in the local area, and aren't mainly for the convenience of you or your doctor.

According to the ICD-9 DM book's introduction, establishing medical necessity is "the first step in third party reimbursement." The diagnosis code submitted with the procedure communicates this medical necessity to the payer.

Medicare and local carriers establish coverage policies for medical services based on the patient's condition, symptoms, or diagnoses. These national and local coverage determinations describe a service and the covered indicators for that service. If a healthcare provider intends to perform one of these services on a Medicare patient who does not have a covered indication or diagnosis, the provider must inform the patient prior to the procedure that it may not or will not be covered. This process of informing the patient prior to providing the service is completed using an Advance Beneficiary Notice.

Related issues:

Medicare also raises the issue of medical necessity in documenting E/M services. The use of templates and electronic health records has increased the volume of medical record documentation for some E/M services. CMS says this about E/M documentation:

> Medical necessity of a service is the overarching criterion for payment in addition to the individual requirements of a CPT® code. It would not be medically necessary or appropriate to bill a higher level of evaluation and management service when a lower level of service is warranted. The volume of documentation should not be the primary influence upon which a specific level of service is billed.

Key points:

- Follow diagnosis coding rules in the ICD-9 book when submitting claims.
- Medical necessity must be supported by the diagnosis code on the claim form and by the medical record.
- NCDs and LCDs are specific coverage policies for healthcare services.
- Use an ABN if you are providing a service to a patient who does not have a covered indication for that service.
- When documenting E/M services using a template or an electronic health record, consider Medicare's warning about the volume of documentation. Do not select an E/M service based solely on the volume of history and exam, if the patient's condition or symptoms did not require that level service.

See also: National Coverage Determinations, Local Coverage Determinations, Advance Beneficiary Notice.

Citations:

Introduction to ICD-9 DM codes

CMS, *Medicare Claims Processing Manual*, Pub 100-04, Chapter 12, Section 30.6.1, http://www.cms.gov/Manuals/IOM/list.asp

Medicare Physician Fee Schedule Data Base (MPFSDB)

Definition:

The MPFSDB is a file published annually by CMS which gives relative value units, as well as other payment status indicators, which direct carriers in the payment of claims.

Explanation:

CMS updates the MPFSDB annually on its web site. The MPFSDB includes relative value units for each CPT® code, geographic adjustments, locality indicators, and explanatory material.

Codes: There are 10,000 CPT® and HCPCS codes included in this file.

Coverage:

Medicare develops information which is then used by its carriers, private payers and physician groups.

Billing and coding rules:

The fee schedule formula determines the payment amount for each covered physician service paid by Part B Medicare. Lab fees are not included, but values for lab services can be found in Medicare's lab fee schedule. The formula for payment is:

2010 Non-Facility Pricing Amount =
[(Work RVU * Work GPCI) +
(Transitioned Non-Facility PE RVU * PE GPCI) +
(MP RVU * MP GPCI)] * Conversion Factor (CF)

2010 Facility Pricing Amount =
[(Work RVU * Work GPCI) +
(Transitioned Facility PE RVU * PE GPCI) +
(MP RVU * MP GPCI)] * CF

The total RVU for a service is the sum of the work RVU, the malpractice expense (MP) RVU, and the practice expense (PE) RVU. Each of these three components is multiplied by the Geographic Practice Cost Indices (GPCI) for the location. That means an appendectomy performed in San Francisco is paid at a different rate than an appendectomy performed in South Dakota. Adding in the locality differences (i.e., the multiplication of the GPCIs in the formula) provides for different payments based on costs for the malpractice and practice expense components. The work GPCI is always one. If the GPCI for your area is less than one, the payment will be less than the national payment amount. If higher than one, the payment will be more than the national payment amount. When negotiating with commercial payers, it is important to know if the contract is based on local or national values, and which will be more beneficial to the practice.

There are two rates: non-facility (i.e., office or home) and facility (e.g., hospital, Ambulatory Surgical Centers, nursing facilities). The same service is paid at a higher rate in a non-facility (i.e., office) than in a facility.

The indicators in this file include a status indicator for each CPT® code; RVUs; global surgery days; surgical code breakdown of pre-surgery, inter-operative work, and post op care; multiple procedure indicator; a bilateral procedure indicator; and an assistant in surgery indicator. The fee schedule also indicates for each relevant procedure code whether co-surgeons or team surgery are payable and those codes covered by the endoscopy payment rules. The level of physician supervision of diagnostic procedures is indicated for diagnostic services.

Related issues:

The MPFSDB answers many questions for physician practices and provides much more information than relative value units.

Key points:
- Download the MPFSDB annually.
- Review the word file that explains the indicators for each CPT® code.

Citations:

CMS, www.cms.gov/PhysicianFeeSched

CMS, *Medicare Claims Processing Manual*, Pub 100-04, Chapter 12, Section 20, http://www.cms.gov/Manuals/IOM/list.asp

Mini Mental Status Exam

Definition:

The mini mental status exam (MMSE) tests cognitive function. One well known example of this test is Folstein's Mini Mental State Exam.

Explanation:

Physicians or NPPs perform a standardized assessment to evaluate their patients' cognitive function. A number of these tests are available. They are typically performed as part of an E/M service.

Code:

There are no codes for mini mental status exam. When performed, the exam is part of an E/M service.

Coverage: As part of an E/M service, it is covered.

Billing and coding rules:

Physicians often want to charge for this assessment as a separate charge item. However, there is no CPT® code for performing a mini mental status exam. In the CPT® book, in the section on central nervous system assessments/test (e.g. neuro-cognitive mental status and speech testing) the CPT® book states: "for mini mental status examination performed by a physician, see evaluation and management code."

A series of codes, 96110–96120, describe psychological tests. It would be incorrect to bill for an MMSE using these any of these codes, however.

Related issues:

The 1997 documentation guidelines include a single specialty psychiatry exam. Clinicians who perform the components of the MMSE may find that using the 1997 guidelines, and the single specialty psychiatry exam in particular, they can more accurately document and bill for the service.

Key points:

- There is no separate billing for an MMSE.
- Bill for this service as part of your evaluation and management service. Examination is one key component when selecting a level of service for an E/M code.
- Look at the single specialty psychiatry exam in the 1997 guidelines.

Citation:

Mini-Mental State Examination, http://www.minimental.com.

Modifier 22

Definition:

Modifier 22 indicates that a service provided was greater than is usual for that CPT® code. It is used on procedure codes, diagnostic tests and procedures in the medicine section, but not E/M services.

Explanation:

Sometimes a physician may wish to indicate that the amount of work for the procedure performed was significantly greater than is typical. This could be because of extensive trauma, patient complications, or patient physical status factors. The CMS manual says this about modifiers for unusual services:

> The fees for services represent the average work effort and practice expenses required to provide a service. For any given procedure code, there could typically be a range of work effort or practice expense required to provide the service. Thus, carriers may increase or decrease the payment for a service only under very unusual circumstances based upon review of medical records and other documentation.

> The CPT® book defines modifier 22 as "Unusual Procedural Services: When the service(s) provided is greater than that usually required for the listed procedure, it may be identified by adding modifier 22 to the usual procedure number."

> Chapter 1 of the NCCI manual adds this information:

> By definition, this modifier would be used in *unusual* circumstances; routine use of the modifier is inappropriate as this practice would suggest cases routinely have unusual circumstances. When an unusual or extensive service is provided, it is more appropriate to utilize modifier -22 than to report a separate code that does not accurately describe the service provided.

Use modifier 22 only for those services that represent significantly more work than is typical. As a rule of thumb, the additional work performed should be 25 to 50% more than normal.

Codes:

Use modifier 22 on anesthesia, surgery, radiology, laboratory, and pathology codes and on procedures in the medicine section.

Coverage:

Medicare and most third party payers recognize the 22 modifier and pay additional reimbursement for its use.

Billing and coding rules:

Append this modifier to the procedure code. Send documentation with the claim that clearly indicates the increased work performed.
The clinician should note the time spent in performing the service.
A brief cover letter that supports and outlines the increased work is usually helpful.

If additional diagnoses support the additional work performed, be sure to document them in the medical record and include them on the claim form.

Increase your fee for this service before you send in the claim.

Related issue:

Do not use modifier 22 on evaluation and management codes. Be sure that the diagnosis coding supports the increased work.

Key points:

- Append when the increased work is 25 to 50% more than is typical for that procedure.
- The documentation should clearly indicate the additional work.
- Send a cover letter which briefly outlines the additional work and will support your claim.
- Use this modifier sparingly in those cases that are outliers.

See also: Modifier 52.

Citations:

CMS, National Correct Coding Initiatives overview, http://www.cms.gov/NationalCorrectCodInitEd

CMS, *Medicare Claims Processing Manual*, Pub 100-04, Chapter 12, Section 20.4.6, http://www.cms.gov/Manuals/IOM/list.asp

Modifier 24

Definition:

Modifier 24 appended to an E/M service indicates that an unrelated E/M service was provided by the same physician during a global post-operative period.

Explanation:

The global payment for a surgical procedure includes the pre-operative work the day of or the day before surgery, the procedure, and the follow up for 0, 10 or 90 days. If the surgeon sees a patient during the global period for a problem unrelated to the surgery, appending modifier 24 to the E/M service allows the claim to be paid per CPT® rules. This indicates that this service was unrelated to the normal global post-operative care.

Codes: This modifier is appended to E/M services.

Coverage:

Most payers recognize modifier 24. However, CMS defines follow up during the post-operative period differently than CPT®. Medicare, per CMS rules, will only pay for complications of surgery if a return trip to the OR is required. The CPT® definition allows payment of E/M services during the post-operative period for complications of the surgery, such as infection or wound dehiscence.

Billing and coding rules:

CPT® codes for surgical procedures are assigned global days (0, 10 or 90 days) in the MPFSDB. Payment for normal post-operative care of the patient by that surgeon or by another surgeon of the same group in the same specialty is included in the fee for that surgery. However, if the patient is seen for an unrelated problem or for abnormal follow up, this service can be billed using a 24 modifier.

Here's an example: An orthopedic surgeon may be seeing a patient for follow up for a knee arthroscopy. The patient, however, returns to the surgeon during that post-operative period with a carpal tunnel problem. That surgeon may bill for this E/M service during the global period by indicating that the carpal tunnel syndrome was not related to the surgery. This is done in two ways on the claim form: append modifier 24 to the E/M code, and use a different diagnosis code than the knee problem.

Medicare has slightly different rules for the global period; it will not pay for any follow up service during the global period unless the patient's condition requires a return trip to the operating room. Commercial insurances may pay for complication of a surgery using the 24 modifier because the CPT® definition of the global period is normal follow up and does not include treatment for complications.

Related issues:

CMS posts the MPFSDB on its web site annually. This fee schedule is the source of significant, important data for physician practices, including the number of post-operative days for each surgical procedure. It downloads in an excel file.

The definition of the global surgical package continues to vary between CMS and the AMA as defined in the CPT® book. This difference requires practices to have separate billing policies depending on the patient's insurance. If possible, when negotiating with third party payers, add in a clause that states that the payer will follow CPT® rules.

Key points:

- Different diagnosis codes are critical when billing with modifier 24.
- If both problems are addressed at the visit, document the new problem carefully.

See also: Global surgical period, Medicare Physician Fee Schedule Data Base

Citations:

CMS, Physician Fee Schedule Overview, www.cms.gov/PhysicianFeeSched/01_overview.asp

CMS, Medicare Claims Processing Manual, Pub 100-04, Chapter 12, Sections 30.6.6, 30.6.8, 30.6.9, 30.6.12, 40

http://www.cms.gov/manuals/IOM/list.asp

Modifier 25

Definition:

Modifier 25 indicates that a significant, separately identifiable evaluation and management service was provided on the same day as a surgical procedure with zero or 10 global days.

The CPT® book defines modifier 25 as follows:

Significant Separately Identifiable Evaluation and Management Service by the Same Physician on the Same Day of the Procedure or Other Service: The physician may need to indicate that on the day a procedure or service identified by a CPT® code was performed, the patient's condition required a significant, separately identifiable E/M service above and beyond the other service provided or beyond the usual pre-operative and post-operative care associated with the procedure that was performed. The E/M service may be prompted by the symptom or condition for which the procedure and/or service was provided. As such, different diagnoses are not required for reporting of the E/M service on the same date. This circumstance may be reported by adding the modifier "25" to the appropriate level of E/M service. Note: This modifier is not used to report an E/M service that resulted in a decision to perform surgery. See modifier "57."

Explanation:

Payers will typically pay for only one service in a day, either an E/M code or a surgery/procedure code. However, modifier 25 allows you to indicate to the payer that you performed a significant, separately identifiable E/M service on the same day as a procedure. Using modifier 25, a practice can be paid for an office visit—or any other E/M service—on the same day as a procedure. Modifier 25 is appended to the E/M service code, not to the procedure code. It is not needed for laboratory work or x-rays taken on the same day as the office visit according to CPT® rules, but some private payer editing systems require it for these services.

Modifier 25 is also used when billing an office visit (99201–99215) on the same day as a preventive medicine service to indicate that a significant, separately identifiable service was done on the same day.

Codes: Applicable to E/M codes.

Coverage: Most national payers recognize modifier 25.

Billing and coding rules:

When using modifier 25, the same diagnosis can be used for the office visit and procedure. For surgical procedures, append the modifier on the E/M service rather than the procedure when the E/M service is more than the typical pre- and post-operative work for the surgical procedure. Typical pre-procedure work includes assessment of the surgical site, querying the patient about contraindications, and obtaining consent. The decision to perform the procedure is included in the payment for the procedure itself.

For Medicare, use this modifier on codes when the procedure has a zero to 10 day global period. If the procedure has a global period of 90 days, use modifier 57.

The clinician should document that the service provided was separate from the surgical procedure. It is more likely to be billable the first time the provider sees a patient for a problem and must perform an assessment prior to doing the procedure. The E/M service is less likely to be a significant, separately identifiable service on visits scheduled for repeat surgical procedures.

For new patients, watch the level of exam that is documented. New patients and consults require all three components at the highest level. If the exam documentation is minimal on the day that the procedure is performed, make sure that the documentation requirements for that code are met. A low level E/M service is indicated in these circumstances. Payment for the decision to perform the procedure is included in the payment for the procedure itself.

Related issues:

In November of 2005, the Office of Inspector General (OIG) reported on an investigation of claims filed with modifier 25, and reported a high error rate. According to the report, in 2002 CMS paid out $1.96 billion for claims that had a modifier 25 submitted. The OIG had certified professional coders review 450 of these claims, and 35% did not meet the program requirement for using modifier 25. In the sample, 35% should not have been billed as an office visit on the same day as the surgical procedure. They also found a large number of claims where modifier 25 was unnecessary.

The OIG recommended that CMS instruct its carriers about the use of modifier 25 and have the carriers work with physicians in learning the rules. The OIG also suggested that CMS should reinforce its requirements for billing an E/M provided on the same day as a surgical procedure. The service documented must entail significantly more pre- and post-work than is typically associated with a surgical procedure. The OIG recommended that carriers emphasize the appropriate documentation of both the E/M service and the surgical procedure. Carriers also should remind physicians that modifier 25 should not be used on claims when only one service (or an x-ray or lab service) was provided was provided on the same day as an E/M service.

Key points:
- Append the modifier to the E/M code, not the surgical code.
- Use modifier 25 if the E/M service was a significant, separately identifiable service.
- Document both services carefully. Be sure that sufficient history, exam, and MDM is documented to justify and E/M service. Document the procedure fully.
- Use modifier 25 when the surgical service has zero or 10 global days.
- Be careful about billing for an office visit and a procedure when the procedure is a scheduled, repeat procedure.
- Different diagnosis codes are not required.

See also: Global surgical period

Citations:

CMS, National Correct Coding Initiatives overview,

http://www.cms.gov/NationalCorrectCodInitEd

OIG, Use of Modifier 25, November 2005, Pub. OEI-07-03-00470, http://oig.hhs.gov/oei/reports/oei-07-03-00470.pdf

Modifier 26

Definition:

When only the professional component of a service is performed for a diagnostic procedure, append modifier 26 to the CPT® code.

Explanation:

Some diagnostic tests have both a technical and a professional component. These can be billed globally without a modifier to indicate that both components of the service were performed. However, in some instances, different physicians or a physician and a hospital may each provide one part of the service.

Codes:

Modifier 26 indicates that the professional component of a diagnostic procedure was provided, while modifier TC indicates that the technical component of a diagnostic service was performed.

Coverage: Most third party payers follow these guidelines.

Billing and coding rules:

Bill for the service performed—the technical component, the professional component, or globally, depending on what you have done in your office.

A common example is in radiology. A patient who receives a chest x-ray at the hospital will receive two bills for that service. The technical component of the chest x-ray will be billed by the hospital, and the professional component (reading the x-ray) will be billed by the radiologist who reads the film. However, if the physician provides this service in the office, owns the equipment, and interprets the x-ray, the physician will bill globally for the service.

The technical component of a diagnostic test includes providing the equipment, the supplies to run the equipment, and paying the staff to perform the test. The professional component includes the professional interpretation of the test.

The professional component is paid only once. An x-ray which is read by an emergency department physician and then later read by a radiologist can only be billed to the third party payer once.

The documentation for the professional component in a physician office should include "radiology-quality reports." It is insufficient to simply sign a machine-generated report. Include in your report the indication for the test, the description of the test, whether it is a 12-lead EKG or a two-view chest X-ray, and the test results.

Related issue:

One of the indicators in the MPFSDB is an indicator that denotes that a diagnostic test has both a technical and a professional component. A practice can also determine if the service has both components by looking at its listing in the MPFSDB. Services that have both components are listed three times: once as the global service, once with the RVUs for the technical component and once with the RVUs for the professional component.

Key points:

- Bill for the service provided: the professional component with a 26 modifier, the technical component with a TC modifier, or globally without a modifier if both were provided.
- The total payment is the same, whether the service is billed globally or by its component parts.
- In order to bill for the technical component, the practice must bear the expense for the service. This includes owning or leasing the equipment, paying for the supplies to perform the test, and paying for the staff to do the test.

See also: Medicare Physician Fee Schedule Data Base

Citations:

CMS, http://www.cms.gov/NationalCorrectCodInitEd/01_overview.asp#TopOfPage

CMS, http://www.cms.gov/PhysicianFeeSched

Modifier 50

Definition:

Modifier 50 is appended to surgical procedures and radiology codes to indicate that a bilateral service was provided on the same patient, by the same provider, during the same session, and the procedure code is not already defined as a bilateral service.

Explanation:

If a bilateral procedure is performed by a physician in one session, the surgeon may indicate that the procedure was bilateral by appending modifier 50 to the CPT® code selected.

Codes:

Modifier 50 is valid on the CPT® codes indicated as status "1" in the MPFSDB in the bilateral indicator field.

Coverage:

Medicare pays 150% of the global amount of a unilateral procedure for bilateral procedures. Most third parties follow along with this guideline.

Billing and coding rules:

CMS requests that the claims for bilateral procedures be submitted to them on a single line on the insurance form with one unit and a 50 modifier appending the procedure code. Some payers, however, prefer to have the claim submitted on two lines. The first line will indicate one unit with that procedure code, while the second line will indicate one unit with the procedure code and a 50 modifier appended. Practices need to check with each payer for instructions on submitting claims for bilateral procedures.

In general, using modifier 50 on a unilateral code will increase your payment.

Read the CPT® definitions carefully, however, because you may not append a 50 modifier to a procedure code that is already defined as bilateral or as "unilateral or bilateral." Review the status indicators for bilateral codes in the Medicare database fee schedule.

Bilateral indicators, per the MFSDB:

0: 150% payment adjustment for bilateral procedures does not apply.

These codes are not eligible for the bilateral modifier because the anatomy or physiology of the human body is such that the procedure could not be done bilaterally or because the CPT® definition specifically describes the service as unilateral.

1: 150% payment adjustment for bilateral procedures apply.

A practice may append the 50 modifier to these surgical or x-ray services and be paid at 150% of the unilateral rate.

2: 150% payment adjustment does not apply.

The payment is already set at 150% because these codes are defined in CPT® as bilateral or the description says, one or both sides, or the procedure is typically performed bilaterally.

3: The usual payment adjustment for bilateral procedures does not apply.

These radiology procedures, when performed on both sides of the body, are not subject to the payment adjustment and will both be paid at full fee.

9: The concept does not apply.

Related issues:

The bilateral code indicator in the Medicare Database Fee Schedule tells physicians whether or not they can append a bilateral modifier to a code.

Key points:

- Check with third party payers about how to submit claims for bilateral services.
- Do not use the bilateral modifier on any procedure that is described in the CPT® book as bilateral.
- Do not use the bilateral indicators on services for which the MFSDB has indicated a zero, two, or nine indicator.
- Some carriers prefer a left and right modifier in place of the bilateral modifier, LT and RT.

See also: Multiple surgical procedures

Citation:

CMS, *Medicare Claims Processing Manual*, Pub 100-04, Chapter 12, Sections 40.6, 40.7, 40.8, http://www.cms.gov/Manuals/IOM/list.asp

Modifier 51

Definition:

Modifier 51 is used when multiple surgical procedures are performed on the same day by the same surgeon. Medicare carriers do not require it.

Explanation:

This modifier is used for multiple surgical procedures performed on the same day by the same surgeon to indicate to the insurance company that a secondary procedure was performed. The first step is to determine which procedure is the primary procedure. The primary procedure is determined by looking at the relative value unit for each procedure, and is the procedure with the highest RVUs. Refer to CMS's MPFSDB for relative value units.

Codes: Append modifier 51 to the second surgical procedure.

Coverage:

CMS does not require this modifier when submitting claims. However, many private payers still use modifier 51.

Billing and coding rules:

When one provider performs multiple surgical procedures on the same day, bill by appending modifier 51 to the secondary procedure (when that procedure is not bundled into the primary procedure).

The primary procedure is paid at 100% of the fee schedule. The payment for the secondary procedure is subject to multiple payment rules. The surgeon is paid less for the second procedure. Medicare assumes that the physician will do the pre- and post-procedure work for the primary procedure and does not need to be paid twice for the same work. Usually, the first procedure is paid at 100%, the second procedure at 50% of the allowed amount, and third and subsequent procedures at 25% of the allowed amount.

Before submitting charges for multiple surgical procedures, always check the MPFSDB, as it determines which procedure has the higher RVU. Bill the procedure with the higher RVU as the primary procedure. Second, check the National Correct Coding Initiative (NCCI) edits. If the procedure is bundled and does not meet the criteria of a separate and distinct procedure, do not bill this second procedure. If the procedure is not bundled, bill it as the second procedure with a 51 modifier.

There is a procedure in this book for determining whether to bill the secondary procedure and whether to use modifier 51 or 59 under the entry, "Multiple surgical procedures."

Related issues:

Some third party payers use a claims editing system that is not based on NCCI edits. This results in denials with such reasons as "this procedure is incidental to the primary procedure." Some practices successfully appeal these on a case-by-case basis by using the NCCI edits as a reference. Other practices have successfully negotiated contracts with third party payers that require the payers to use the NCCI edits when processing claims.

Key points:

- When performing multiple surgical procedures, check the relative value units for each procedure. The procedure with the highest RVUs is the primary procedure.
- If the second procedure is a component of the first, and the second does not meet the criteria of "separate," do not bill the second procedure.

See also: Modifier 59, modifier 50, multiple surgical procedures

Citations:

CMS, National Correct Coding Initiatives overview, http://www.cms.gov/NationalCorrectCodInitEd

CMS, *Medicare Claims Processing Manual*, Pub 100-04, Chapter 12, Section 40.6, http://www.cms.gov/Manuals/IOM/list.asp

Modifier 52

Definition:

Modifier 52 indicates to the payer that significantly less work was done than would be typical for a particular procedure.

Explanation:

This modifier is appended to a surgical service code to indicate that the amount of work performed for that service was less than typical.

Codes:

According to CPT® instructions, you can use modifier 52 with a medical or a surgical procedure code. However, CMS only recognizes modifier 52 when appended to surgical procedure codes.

Coverage: Recognized by many payers.

Billing and coding rules:

The definition for a surgical procedure describes all of the criteria that are required in order to bill for that service. If the physician performs only part of that service, however, and there is no other CPT® code which more accurately describes the lesser amount of work done, append modifier 52 to the service.

Related issue:

Do not use this modifier if the procedure was cancelled after the induction of anesthesia but before the service was commenced.

Key points:

- Practices will usually need to send notes along with the claim for this service.
- Do not use modifier 52 for discontinued services.
- The *Medicare Claims Processing Manual* specifically tells clinicians not to use this code for reduced E/M services.

See also: Modifier 22, Modifier 53

Citation:

CMS, *Medicare Claims Processing Manual*, Pub 100-04, Chapter 12, Section 30.6.1B, http://www.cms.hhs.gov/Manuals/IOM/list.asp

Modifier 53

Definition:

Modifier 53 is used for a discontinued procedure. According to the CPT® book, use it when the physician elects to terminate a surgical or diagnostic procedure due to circumstances that threaten the patient. Report the CPT® code of the discontinued procedure with modifier 53.

Explanation:

Modifier 53 is used on surgical or medical diagnostic procedures to indicate that the procedure was discontinued after anesthesia was administered to the patient due to a threat to the patient's wellbeing. It is not used to report a procedure, which was cancelled prior to anesthesia induction and/or surgical preparation in the operating room.

Codes:

Use on surgical codes or medical diagnostic codes. It cannot be used with E/M services.

Coverage:

Most payers recognize the modifier. The service is paid at a reduced rate.

Billing and coding rules:

The chart should describe the clinical circumstances leading to the decision to stop the procedure. The note should indicate how much of the procedure was performed. Typically, the patient will be re-scheduled for the procedure. It is incorrect to use Modifier 53 when a procedure is converted from a laparoscopic procedure to an open procedure. In that case, bill only for the open procedure.

Related issues:

Not all modifiers effect payment, but all communicate to the payer that the circumstances related to the provision of service is different in some way.

Key points:

- Modifier 52 is used to describe reduced services. In that case, the procedure is completed, but not all components as described by the CPT® code were performed.
- Modifier 53 is used when the patient's well being is threatened if the procedure is continued. The patient must have been prepped for the

service in the operating suite and/or have anesthesia, and then the physician decided to stop the procedure.

See also: Modifier 22, Modifier 52

Citations:

CPT® Book, CPT® Assistant, Coding with Modifiers: A Guide to Correct CPT® and HCPCS Modifier Usage 3rd Edition, by Deborah J Grider, published by the AMA

Modifier 58

Definition:

Using modifier 58 on a procedure or service indicates that a staged or related procedure was performed by the same physician, subsequent to an initial service during the global period.

Explanation:

Use this modifier to report a staged procedure, which was planned at the time of the first procedure, or to indicate that the second procedure was more extensive than the first. It may also be used for a therapeutic service after a diagnostic one. Only use it during the surgical post op period for the first procedure.

Codes:

Use on surgical codes. It cannot be used with E/M services.

Coverage:

Most payers recognize the modifier.

Billing and coding rules:

An example of when to use modifier 58 is for a patient who had a breast biopsy, which has a ten day global period. If the patient needs to return to the operating room for a more extensive procedure on the breast as a result of the biopsy, use modifier 58 on the second, staged procedure.

Related issues:

Physicians and coders must review the global days for the primary procedure in order to correctly assign modifiers during the global period. Physicians of the same specialty in the same group should bill as if they were one physician. That is, if a physician's partner does the second planned surgery, use the same modifier as if the first physician had performed the service.

Key points:

- Use modifier 58 on the subsequent service for a planned or staged procedure.
- A new post op period begins at the date of the second procedure.
- Use this modifier during the post op period, starting the day after the first procedure.

- Do not use this modifier for complications of the first procedure that require a return trip to the OR. Use modifier 78 for procedures performed as a result of complications.
- Use this when the second surgery is related to the first, performed by the same physician and in the global period.

See also: Modifier 78 and 79

Citations:

www.wpsmedicare.com/part_b/education/modifier_78.pdf

www.wpsmedicare.com/part_b/education/modifier_79.pdf

Modifier 59

Definition:
Modifier 59 is a modifier of last resort, to be used only when no other modifiers accurately reflect the care provided. Chapter one of the National Correct Coding Initiative (NCCI) manual describes modifier 59 as follows:

> Modifier -59: Modifier -59 is an important NCCI-associated modifier that is often used incorrectly. For the NCCI its primary purpose is to indicate that two or more procedures are performed at different anatomic sites or different patient encounters. It should only be used if no other modifier more appropriately describes the relationships of the two or more procedure codes.

Explanation:
Modifier 59 bypasses NCCI bundling edits and allows a surgeon to bill for a secondary procedure that is bundled into the primary procedure. However, the secondary procedure must meet the criteria of being distinct and separate. This means that it is performed during a different session or encounter; on a different site or organ system; on a separate lesion, incision, or excision; or for a separate injury.

Codes: Surgical codes, lab codes, and procedures in the medicine section.

Coverage: All payers.

Billing and coding rules:
What constitutes a distinct and separate service? According to the NCCI, this could be a different session or patient encounter, a different site or organ system, a separate lesion, incision, or excision, or a separate injury. Different diagnosis codes are not required for Modifier 59 use. Use this modifier carefully.

Related issues:
The OIG issued a report on the use of Modifier 59 in November 2005. It found widespread error in the use and payment of this modifier.

Key points:
Append modifier 59 to a secondary procedure code when:
- the secondary procedure is a component of the first procedure **and**

- there is no other modifier that more accurately describes the service **and**
- the secondary procedure meets the distinct and separate services definition.

See also: Medicare Physician Fee Schedule Database, multiple surgical procedures

Citations:

CMS, *Medicare Claims Processing Manual*, Pub 100-04, Chapter 12, Sections 40.6, 40.7, 40.8, http://www.cms.gov/Manuals/IOM/list.asp

OIG, *Use of Modifier 59 to Bypass Medicare's National Correct Coding Initiative*, November 2005, Pub. OEI-03-02-00771, http://oig.hhs.gov/oei/reports/oei-03-02-00771.pdf

CMS, National Correct Coding Initiatives overview, http://www.cms.gov/NationalCorrectCodInitEd

Modifier 78 and Modifier 79

Definition:

Modifier 78 is used to indicate that a return trip to the operating room that is related to the original surgery was required during a global post-operative period. Modifier 79 is used to indicate that a return trip to the OR was required that was unrelated to the original surgery, during the global post-operative period.

Explanation:

The global post-operative period includes follow up care for surgeries for the number of days indicated in the MPFSDB. If a return trip to the OR is required during that post-op period, the surgeon must use a modifier in order to be paid.

Codes: Modifiers 78 and 79 are used on procedures.

Coverage: All payers.

Billing and coding rules:

When using modifier 78, Medicare will pay only for the intra-operative portion of the code. CMS considers that the surgeon is already being paid for the pre- and post-op work from the original surgery. Use this modifier when a complication of the original procedure requires a return trip to the OR. A new global period does not begin on the date of the second procedure.

Modifier 79 indicates that the second surgical procedure was performed by the same surgeon but was unrelated to the first surgical procedure. A different diagnosis should be submitted.

For cataract operations, some payers require modifier 79 to indicate that the second operation was performed on the other eye within the 90-day global period from the first procedure. A second global period starts on the date of the second procedure when modifier 79 is used.

Related issues:

Medicare only pays for complications in the post-op period if a return trip to the OR is required.

Key points:

- Append modifier 78 to a surgical procedure during the global period for a return trip to the OR that is related to the first surgery.

- Append modifier 79 to the surgical procedure during the global period for a return trip to the OR by the same surgeon that is unrelated to the original surgery.
- Modifier 58 is used for a staged or planned return trip to the OR.

See also: Global period, Modifier 58.

Citation:

CMS, *Medicare Claims Processing Manual*, Pub 100-04, Chapter 12, Section 40, http://www.cms.gov/Manuals/IOM/list.asp

Multiple Endoscopy Procedures

Definition:

Medicare payment rules for multiple endoscopy procedures allow 100% of the primary procedure, plus the difference between the next highest valued procedure and the base procedure.

Explanation:

Physician payment for multiple endoscopies do not follow the usual multiple surgical payment rule. Payment is based on the family of endoscopy codes performed. Medicare and most insurers pay for the base payments in the family of codes only once. This means that for subsequent endoscopy procedures, the payment for the base is subtracted from the payment for subsequent services provided.

Codes: Endoscopy codes.

Coverage: Medicare and most other payers.

Billing and coding rules:

These codes are identified in the Medicare Physician Fee Schedule Database, by a three in field 21. When billing for multiple endoscopies, check the National Correct Coding Initiative edits. The base procedure in each family of codes is bundled into more complex codes in the series and may not be billed with the higher complexity code with any modifier. These are indicated as separate procedures in the CPT® book.

Many carriers do not require modifier 51 on the subsequent endoscopic procedures. Although applying modifier 51 meets the CPT® coding rules, check with your carrier and third party payers before using it. If the second endoscopic procedure meets the criteria of a different or separate procedure, such as a different lobe or procedure performed at a different surgical session, apply the 59 modifier to the second procedure.

Related issues:

The reimbursement for secondary endoscopic procedures is low.

Key points:

- Check the NCCI edits for bundled procedures.
- Bill primary procedure with no modifier.

- Do not bill the diagnostic base procedure in a family of codes when billing more complex codes in that family.
- Bill secondary procedures with a modifier 51, or with no modifier if so instructed by your carrier or third party payer.
- Bill secondary procedures that meet the criteria of a separate and distinct service with a 59 modifier.

See also: Multiple surgical procedures, modifier 51, modifier 59.

Citations:

CMS, *Medicare Claims Processing Manual*, Pub 100-04, chapter 12, Section 40.6, http://www.cms.gov/Manuals/IOM/list.asp

NCCI introductory chapter: http://www.cms.gov/NationalCorrectCodInitEd

Multiple Surgical Procedures

Definition:

Surgeons are paid at 100% of the fee schedule amount for the primary surgical procedure, at 50% for the second surgical procedure, and at 25% for the third to fifth surgical procedure performed at the same surgical session.

Explanation:

Billing for multiple surgical procedures performed at the same session depends on bundling rules, NCCI edits, correct modifier use, and relative value units. In order to bill successfully for providing multiple surgical services on the same day, the physician needs to understand all of these coding rules.

Codes: Surgical procedures.

Coverage: All payers.

Billing and coding rules:

When performing multiple surgical procedures, physicians should code the major procedure with no modifier. The major procedure is the procedure with the highest relative value units in the Medicare Physicians Fee Schedule Database. Additional procedures, which are not component codes of the major procedure, are reported with modifier 51. Although it is correct coding, not all payers and carriers require modifier 51.

Additional procedures which are components of the first procedure and do not meet the criteria for being distinct and separate are not submitted to the carrier. These are bundled or included in the payment for the primary procedure. When an additional procedure is a component and meets the criteria for being distinct and separate, use modifier 59.

According to the *Medicare Claims Processing Manual*, bilateral surgeries are surgeries performed on both sides of the body by the same surgeon during the same session on the same day. If the surgical definition of the service is bilateral or says "unilateral or bilateral," the multiple surgery rules do not apply. Payment is already based on the service as a bilateral service. If the code description is "bilateral" the claim should not be submitted with the bilateral modifier. Bilateral surgeries are paid at 150% of the physician's fee schedule amount.

Related issues:

When using modifier 59 to bill for the second procedure, be sure that the second procedure meets the criteria of a distinct, separate service. Distinct and separate means that the service was provided at a different session or patient encounter; on a different organ or site; on a separate lesion; or for a different incision, excision, or injury. Do not apply it to the second service if it is not a component code of the first. Do not use it to bypass NCCI edit if the second service does not meet the criteria of the distinct and separate.

Key points:

Use this procedure when submitting claims for multiple surgical procedures.

1. List all codes for the procedures performed.
2. Note whether the procedures were performed via the same compartment, incision, site, organ system, lesion, injury, during the same session, and by the same surgeon. If all are the same, note "same." If any of the above are different, note "different."
3. Check the RVUs for each procedure and note them next to the code. The code with the highest RVU is the primary procedure; the others are secondary procedures. Note the primary procedure.
4. Check the CCI edits. If the secondary procedures are component codes of the primary procedures, and the procedure is the same (as indicated above), bill only the primary procedure.
5. If the secondary procedures are not component codes of the primary procedure, and the procedure is the same (as defined above), bill the primary procedure with no modifier and the secondary procedures with modifier 51. This indicates that multiple procedures were performed that fall into the category of "same" as indicated above.
6. If the secondary procedures are component codes of the primary procedure, but the procedure meets the difference criteria above (different session, compartment, lesion, injury, etc.), bill the primary procedure with no modifier and bill the secondary procedures with modifier 59.

See also: Multiple endoscopy procedures, Medical Physician Fee Schedule Database, modifier 50, modifier 51, modifier 59.

Citations:

CMS, *Medicare Claims Processing Manual*, Pub 100-04, Chapter 12, Sections 40.6, 40.7, 40.8, http://www.cms.gov/Manuals/IOM/list.asp

OIG, http://oig.hhs.gov/oei/reports/oei-03-02-00771.pdf
(for the modifier 59 report from the OIG)

National Correct Coding Initiative (NCCI)

Definition:

The National Correct Coding Initiative Edits are CMS developed edits for the purpose of processing claims correctly and controlling improper or incorrect payments to providers.

Explanation:

The NCCI edits define payment policies to ensure uniform and correct payments to physicians and other healthcare providers. Services denied by Medicare due to NCCI edits may not be billed to Medicare beneficiaries, whether or not the provider obtained an ABN. There are two types of edits. The first set is for comprehensive and component code edits, commonly known as bundling edits, in which the provider must select the most comprehensive code. The second is for mutually exclusive edits, which describe services that may not be billed together. Certain modifiers allow a claim to bypass the NCCI edits, and these modifiers must be applied correctly in order to insure both revenue collection and compliance.

If carriers apply these edits uniformly, it reduces the variation in how claims are processed amongst carriers.

Codes:

The NCCI edits include thousands of code pairs and are updated quarterly.

Coverage:

These are Medicare edits, but they are adopted by many other carriers. Some carriers develop their own edits.

Billing and coding rules:

All practices need to check the NCCI edits for services they perform, when the same physician provides more than one service to the same patient on the same day. There are three ways to do this. The first is to download a free copy of these edits from the CMS web site. Practices no longer have to buy the NCCI edits. The web site address is in the citation section of this entry. A second, easier way to use the NCCI edits is to buy a computer program or subscribe to a web site that allows the user to type in the procedure codes and check for bundling edits or mutually exclusive code pairs. All of the major commercial providers of coding books have single and multi-user computer systems available. There are web based subscription programs available. The NCCI edits on paper are notoriously difficult to use and understand, so a computer-based system is preferable. The third option available to some practices is a claims editor integrated with a billing system. This is a terrific option if available from the billing vendor.

The introduction to the NCCI manual defines what services are included in the surgical procedure. This includes vascular and airway access and cardiac monitoring, anesthesia provided by the physician who is performing the service, non-diagnostic biopsies, exploration of the surgical field, access through abnormal tissue, incision and opening, treatment of complications such as bleeding, unless a return to the operating room is required. This introduction provides an important overview to NCCI. A copy of it can be downloaded in the manual section from CMS. It is titled, "NCCI Policy Manual for Part B Medicare Carriers."

The modifiers that bypass the NCCI edits include modifier 22, unusual procedural service, modifier 25, significant, separately identifiable service, modifier 50, bilateral procedure, modifier 58, staged or related procedure by the same physician during the post op period, and modifier 59, separate procedure.

In late 2005, the OIG released two reports about the use of modifier 25 and modifier 59. They noted a high error rate in paid claims for both of these. Since both bypass the claims editing system and allow a physician to be paid, the OIG is concerned about overpayments due to the incorrect use of these modifiers to bypass claims editing rules.

Key points:
- Download and read the introductory material to the NCCI edits.
- Check for bundled procedures and mutually exclusive procedures prior to billing the services provided, when more than one service is provided by the same physician, on the same date, to the same patient.
- Consider using a computer-based program to check NCCI edits.
- Do not bill the patient, with or without an ABN, for procedures denied because they are mutually exclusive or bundled.
- Review the rules related to modifiers 25 and 59.

See also: Modifier 25, modifier 59, multiple surgical procedures

Citations:

CMS, http://www.cms.gov/NationalCorrectCodInitEd/01_overview.asp#TopOfPage

Medicare Claims Processing Manual, Pub 100-04, Chapter 23
http://www.cms.gov/Manuals/IOM/list.asp

National Coverage Determinations (NCDs)

Definition:

National Coverage Determinations are statements of Medicare policy that describe coverage and limitations for selected services.

Explanation:

Medicare pays for services that it considers "reasonable and necessary for the diagnosis or treatment of an illness or injury." CMS bases its determinations on evidence-based medicine, and it allows physicians and other members of the public to comment on proposed NCDs.

Codes:

There is a long list of laboratory services and other procedures covered by these policies.

Coverage:

These are Medicare policies but they, or similar policies, are often adopted by other payers.

Billing and coding rules:

The CMS web site has a list of NCDs and Local Coverage Determinations that can be searched by keyword or accessed alphabetically. Each NCD notes the publication number, manual section, version, effective and implementation dates, benefit categories (such as diagnostic tests, physician services, and durable medical equipment) and coverage topics (such as diagnostic tests and durable medical equipment). The services described and the covered clinical indications for the service or test are listed. The NCDs also describe non-covered indications. For some policies, frequency limitations are listed. The policy lists cross-references to CMS transmittals to the manuals, and to transmittal links.

Payers typically pay based on CPT® codes but deny based on the diagnosis code. Submitting a claim for which there is an NCD when the patient does not have a covered indication will result in a denial. In plain English, Medicare does not cover the service for that condition or diagnosis. Using the NCDs allows the practice to discuss non-covered services with the patient prior to providing the service. The practice then has the opportunity to obtain an Advance Beneficiary Notice (ABN) from the patient, if the physician and patient want to continue with the service. The patient will be financially liable for the service if an ABN is properly executed.

Related issues:

Medicare and all third party payers use medical necessity as a key determining factor in deciding whether to pay or deny a claim. NCDs are a way that Medicare has attempted to standardize coverage indications and limitations for services, using evidence-based medicine. Physician practices and individual patients do not always agree with these decisions.

Key points:

- Research NCDs for services provided in the practice.
- If a patient does not have a covered indication for the service as indicated in the NCD, inform the patient before providing the service, or before prepping the patient for the service, that it is non-covered.
- Properly execute an ABN if the patient wishes to proceed.
- Educate your staff about ABNs and assign responsibility for explaining coverage to the patient and obtaining an ABN.
- If possible, build these rules into your claims processing systems so the posting staff is alerted at the time of posting if the diagnosis code and the procedure code do not match.

See also: Advance Beneficiary Notice, Local Coverage Determinations, medical necessity

Citations:

CMS, http://www.cms.gov/DeterminationProcess

Alphabetical listing: http://www.cms.gov/mcd/index_list.asp?list_type=ncd

Search by topic/state: http://www.cms.gov/mcd/search.asp?

New Patient

Definition:

A new patient is a patient who has not received any professional service from the physician or from another physician of the same specialty in the same group within the past three years.

Explanation:

Office visit codes and preventive medicine services are divided into new and established patient visits. A new patient is defined by time limits, by the specialty of the physician, and by the physician's membership in the group. A professional service is any face-to-face medical, surgical, or diagnostic service.

Codes: Office visits and preventive medicine services.

Coverage:

Both the CPT® definition and the Medicare definition of a new patient are the same.

Billing and coding rules:

Bill an established patient visit if the patient has been seen by that physician or by another physician of the same specialty in the same group within the past three years.

Here are some "what if" scenarios.

What if a physician changes groups within the same town? A physician who sees a patient and then joins a new group in the same town will bring many of his or her own patients to the new practice. Because the physician has provided a professional service in the past three years, these are considered established patient visits in the new office.

What if a physician sees a patient for the first time in the hospital, and the patient follows up in the office? A physician who sees the patient in the hospital and then sees the patient for the first time in his or her office should bill for an established patient visit, because the physician had a recent face-to-face service with the patient in the hospital.

What about covering for another physician? A physician who is covering for another physician in the group of the same specialty, even if he or she is not seeing the patient personally, will also bill for an established patient visit if the patient is considered established to the first physician.

Be careful when there are multiple locations of the same specialty in the same group. Under Medicare guidelines, pay for physicians in a group of the same specialty as if they were one physician, even if they practice in a different location. This definition of group membership has a large impact on the definition of new patient visits. However, physicians of different specialties may both see a patient and bill an office visit service on the same date. Similarly, preventive care services are divided into new and established patient visits, and the same rules apply.

Related issues:

Many Evaluation and Management services are not categorized as new and established, including consultations, hospital services, emergency department visits, and nursing home services.

Key points:

- Bill for physicians in a group of the same specialty as if they were one physician.
- A new patient is a patient who has not had a professional service from that physician or from another physician of the same specialty within the past 3 years.
- Be careful when billing for physicians of one specialty who practice in multiple locations.
- Remember, neither a new chart nor a new problem indicates a new patient.

See also: Consultations.

Citation:

CMS, *Medicare Claims Processing Manual*, Pub 100-04, Chapter 12, Sections 30.6.5 and 30.6.7, http://www.cms.gov/Manuals/IOM/list.asp

Nurse Visit

Definition:

The lowest level Evaluation and Management established patient visit provided by a nurse or nursing assistant in the physician office can be billed as a nurse visit.

Explanation:

Established patient visits have five levels of service. The lowest level of service, 99211, may be billed by a nurse. The CPT® book tells us that this service may not require a face-to-face visit from a physician. There are no explicit documentation requirements for this code, but the service must be documented in the medical record.

Code: 99211.

Coverage:

A practice must meet the requirements for incident to services to bill a nurse visit to a Medicare patient. Other payers' coverage varies.

Billing and coding rules:

The most important billing rule to remember for Medicare patients is that in order to bill with code 99211, the service must meet the criteria for incident to rules. Other payers' rules will vary, of course. Like all medical services, a nurse visit must be medically necessary. Practices should not use this code automatically in addition to another service on a routine basis, such as an allergy injection or flu shot. Do not use 99211 when the service provided is more accurately described by another CPT® code, such as vaccine administration or venipuncture. The nurse who sees the patient should document in the progress note section of the chart, not just on the flow sheet. The nurse who performs the service should provide a separate note which would typically include the reason for the visit, a brief history, exam (such as vital signs), and a brief assessment and plan. The plan may describe the patient's medications or any discussion with the physician.

A blood pressure check is a typical reason for a nurse visit on a Medicare patient. For non-Medicare patients, a nurse might address a new problem covered under an office protocol, such as a urinary tract infection. This would not be appropriate on a Medicare patient, because new problems do not meet the criteria of incident to services.

Related issues:

Sometimes, practices want to bill a nurse visit on the same day that a patient sees a physician or NPP. No payers will pay for a 99211 in addition to an office visit on the same day.

Key points:

- For Medicare, the service must meet incident to requirements.
- The nursing staff member should sign and date the note for that visit.
- Do provide separate documentation.
- Do not automatically bill a nurse visit with another service, such as an allergy injection.
- Remember, medical necessity is the key to providing all medical services.
- Do not bill a nurse visit in place of another service which is more accurately described by another CPT® code.

See also: Documentation Guidelines, incident to services.

Citation:

CMS, *Medicare Claims Processing Manual*, Pub. 100-04, Sections 20.3, 30.5, 30.6.4, http://www.cms.gov/Manuals/IOM/list.asp

Nursing Facility Visits

Definition:

Nursing facility visits are Evaluation and Management services performed in a skilled nursing facility or a nursing facility.

Explanation:

As of January 1, 2006, the AMA released a new set of nursing facility codes. Most of the old nursing facility codes were deleted as of January 31, 2005, and may no longer be used. There is no grace period for deleted CPT® codes.

Nursing facility codes may be used in place of service 31 for patients in a Part A covered skilled nursing facilities. They can be used in place of service code 32 for patients in non-Part A covered skilled nursing facility beds, in non-covered skilled nursing facilities, or in nursing facilities.

Who may bill for nursing home codes? Physicians and NPPs may bill for nursing facility codes, but only a physician may bill for initial nursing facility care (99304–99306) to a skilled nursing facility. After the initial service has been provided, a physician and an NPP may alternate providing subsequent nursing facility care (99307–99310). Although it does not make much sense from the code descriptions, an NPP may provide the subsequent nursing facility care to a patient before the physician performs and bills for the initial nursing facility care.

In a nursing facility, (as differentiated from a skilled nursing facility) NPPs who are not employed by the nursing facility may bill for the initial service as long as that service is within their scope of practice, meets their state law, and meets collaboration and supervision requirements. An NPP in a nursing facility may bill for all of the subsequent nursing facility visits.

There are two levels of nursing facility discharge, one for a discharge that takes the provider 30 minutes or less, and one for a discharge that takes more than 30 minutes to complete. This is the total time of the discharge, not the face-to-face time with the patient.

The code for an annual assessment is now 99318.

Codes:

99304–99306	Initial nursing facility care
99307–99310	Subsequent nursing facility care
99315–99316	Nursing facility discharge services
99318	Other nursing facility services (annual assessment)

Coverage: Visits covered based on patient status in the nursing facility.

Billing and coding rules:

The physician must bill for the initial admission service in the skilled nursing facility. After that, the physician and the NPP may alternate visits. NPPs may bill for subsequent nursing facility visits before or after the physician has performed the admission. This can be useful when the physician does not get to the nursing facility within the first day or two to see the patient. The NPP can bill for a subsequent nursing facility visit even before that admission was performed.

In a nursing facility, the NPP may perform all subsequent nursing visits.

Although it is usually difficult to successfully bill for two E/M services in one day, a physician may be paid for both a discharge from the hospital and an admission to the nursing facility on the same date. However, the physician may not use the discharge service as the admission and bill for both. The physician must see and discharge the patient in the hospital in order to bill 99238 or 99239, and then the physician must have a face-to-face service with the patient in the skilled nursing facility in order to bill for the initial skilled nursing facility service.

Nursing facility services do have typical times in the CPT® book.

Related issues:

How frequently must the physician or NPP see a patient who is in a skilled nursing facility? A visit is required within 30 days of the admission, every 30 days within the first 90 days of care, and every 60 days after that.

If the clinician is asked to see a patient for a medical problem, that visit may be used as one of the required visits; the clinician need not provide the medically necessary service one day and then do the mandated review service the day after that. Skilled nursing services may not be billed as incident to or shared visits. If an NPP performs the service in a nursing facility, bill under the NPP provider number, not the physician's provider number.

Key points:

- All nursing facilities are per day codes by CPT® definition. Only one nursing home visit can be billed and paid in a single day.
- The physician must bill for the admission to the skilled nursing facility.

- An NPP may bill for an admission to the nursing facility in certain situations. The NPP must not be an employee of the nursing facility and it must be within that NPP's scope of practice, allowed by state law, and covered under applicable supervision requirements.
- After the initial service in the skilled nursing facility the MD and the NPP may alternate visits.
- A physician may delegate all nursing facility visits to an NPP.
- The place of service billed is based on the designation of the patient: a skilled nursing facility is POS 31 and a nursing facility is POS 32.
- Providers must meet frequency requirements for nursing facility patients.
- A medically necessary visit or an annual assessment can count as one of the mandated visits according to the frequency requirements.

See also: Consolidated nursing home billing.

Citations:

CMS, *Medicare Claims Processing Manual*, Pub 100-04, Chapter 12, Section 30.6.13, http://www.cms.gov/Manuals/IOM/list.asp

OIG Work Plan

Definition:

The Office of Inspector General (OIG) is one arm of the Department of Health and Human Services. Each year, the OIG publishes its Work Plan, which briefly describes its projects for the upcoming year.

Explanation:

The OIG web site describes the mission of the OIG as the protection of the integrity of the Department of Health and Human Services, as well as the health and welfare of the beneficiaries of these programs. The mission of the OIG is to ensure that taxpayer money spent by CMS complies with all coverage, billing, and coding rules. The OIG also protects the individual beneficiary with regard to the payment of health services.

Codes: All.

Coverage: Medicare and Medicaid.

Billing and coding rules:

The OIG Work Plan is published online in October of each year. This Work Plan, and the plans from previous fiscal years, are available for download. The Work Plan is divided into sections, with one section covering physician services.

The section on physician services is three to four pages long and lists upcoming projects, also giving a brief description of each project's focus. For example, the following appeared in the 2006 OIG Work Plan:

Care Plan Oversight

We will evaluate the efficacy of controls over Medicare payments for care plan oversight claims submitted by physicians. Care plan oversight exists where there is physician supervision of patients in hospice care that require complex or multidisciplinary modalities involving regular physician and/or revision of care plans. Reimbursement for care plan oversight increased from $15 million in 2000 to $41 million in 2001. We will assess whether these services were provided in accordance with Medicare regulations. (OAS; W-00-04-35114; various reviews; expected issue date: FY 2006; work in progress)

The OIG web site specifically states that it does not provide additional explanation about why a subject was selected or what type of errors are being investigated for that subject. Each year, physician practices should review the OIG Work Plan to see what services that they provide are listed as projects. For example, if the physician bills for care plan oversight, knowing that the OIG was interested in the topic, the practice would be advised to review the billing and coding rules and audit their own records for compliance.

Related issues:

Physician compliance plans need to be reviewed and updated annually. Too many physicians re-audit the same services annually without considering areas of risk, new billing activities, and volume of services. Reviewing CERT reports, RAC targets and the OIG Work Plan can guide practices about the topics to include in their own compliance plans.

Key points:

- The OIG publishes a Work Plan each October that outlines and briefly describes the agency's projects for the coming year. The Work Plan is available on the OIG's web site.
- Physician practices should review the list of OIG projects for services they provide. Also review the coverage, billing, and coding rules for any services performed in the practice that are mentioned in the Work Plan.

See also: Comprehensive Error Rate Testing and Recovery Audit Contractors

Citations:

OIG, http://oig.gov/publications/workplan.html

Patient Protection and Affordable Care Act (PPACA) aka Health Care Reform Act of 2010

Definition:

Congress passed health care reform legislation in 2010 after a long and protracted political battle. This act changes the law regarding health care insurance coverage in a significant way, requiring all Americans to buy health insurance or pay a penalty. The act also included changes for physician practices in Medicare and in the area of compliance.

Explanation:

This large bill has many components which will affect physician practices. More patients will be covered by private insurers and by Medicaid. Compliance activities in physician practices change from "recommended" to mandatory. Primary care gets a payment boost from 2011–2016. The PQRI program is permanent, and there is a penalty for not reporting on quality indicators. Congress continues talking about moving from fee-for-service healthcare to paying for quality.

Codes: All

Coverage: Varies by portion of the act

Billing and coding rules:

The bill provides for a number of pilot projects that continue to move payment for Medicare services from fee-for-service to paying for quality. In 2015, there is a penalty of 1.5% of Medicare payments for not reporting on PQRI. The Secretary of CMS must establish a values-based modifier by 2012, which reflects health outcomes, and develop a program to implement its use by 2015. This will be budget neutral, resulting in higher payments for those who participate and lower payments for those who don't.

Between 2011 and 2016 there will be a 10% bonus payment for primary care services provided by pediatricians, internists, family physicians, geriatricians and physician assistants, nurse practitioners and clinical nurse specialists working in primary care. At least 60% of their charges must be for office visits, home visits or nursing facility visits in order to be eligible.

The law also establishes an Independent Advisory Board to slow the per capita growth rate of Medicare without rationing care or increasing premiums. (Is magic allowed?)

The bill makes changes in preventive services for both commercially insured patients and Medicare patients. Starting in January, 2011, Medicare will pay for an annual wellness exam. As this book goes to print, they have not defined that exam, but will probably develop an HCPCS code to define the service, in place of the CPT® codes in the 99381–99397 series. Any service that is given an A or B rating by the US Preventive Task Force will be covered by Medicare in the future.

There are limits on physician-owned hospitals. Any hospital not enrolled and credentialed by the end of 2010 will no longer be approved.

Key points:
- CMS continues to emphasize reporting on quality of care, using an electronic health record and E-prescribing. There are a number of pilot and demonstration projects that emphasize quality and effectiveness over fee-for-service.
- An annual wellness exam will be covered starting January 1, 2011.
- Primary care clinicians will get a boost in payment from 2011–2016.

See also: Wellness visit

Citations:
https://www.cms.gov/LegislativeUpdate/downloads/PPACA.pdf

Pelvic and Breast Clinical Exam

Definition:

A pelvic and clinical breast exam is a physical screening service described by Medicare using code G0101, cervical or vaginal screening, pelvic and clinical breast exam.

Explanation:

Medicare was created not for routine services, but for the treatment of illness or injury. Over the years, however, Congress has passed provisions that allow Medicare to pay for certain screening services within diagnosis code and time limitations. Medicare also pays for certain immunizations. The pelvic and breast exam is one example of a covered screening service.

In addition to paying for the pelvic and breast exam, Medicare will pay for obtaining and preparing the specimen for a PAP smear using code Q0091. Codes G0101 and Q0091 are covered annually for high risk patients, and every other year for low risk patients.

There are specific exam elements required, as outlined below.

Codes:

G0101 Cervical or vaginal cancer screening; pelvic and clinical breast examination

Q0091 Screening Papanicolaou smear; obtaining, preparing and conveyance of cervical or vaginal smear to laboratory

Billing and coding rules:

Medicare pays for a pelvic exam every two years for low risk patients and annually for high risk patients. The diagnosis code for the bi-annual screening is V76.2 (special screening for malignant neoplasm, cervical); for the annual exam it is V15.89 (other specified personal history presenting hazards to health). Codes V76.47, V76.49, and V72.31 are also covered diagnoses for this service.

High risk factors for cervical or vaginal cancer include the following:

1. Early onset of sexual activity (under 16 years of age)
2. Multiple sexual partners (five or more in a lifetime)
3. History of sexually transmitted diseases
4. Fewer than three negative pap smears within the previous seven years
5. Diethylstilbestrol (DES)-exposed daughters of women who took DES during pregnancy

G0101 (Cervical or vaginal screening; pelvic and clinical breast exam) is used to bill for the exam. This exam should include seven of the 11 elements below and must include a breast exam:

- Inspection and palpation of the breasts for masses, lumps, tenderness, asymmetry, or nipple discharge
- Digital rectal exam

Pelvic exam, including:
- External genitalia
- Urethral meatus
- Bladder
- Urethra
- Vagina
- Cervix
- Uterus
- Adnexa/parametria
- Anus and perineum

This service may be done on the same day as a covered E/M service (office visit), or on the same day as a non-covered physical exam. If done on the same day as an E/M service, attach the 25 modifier on the office visit.

If the pelvic and breast exam is done on the same day as a non-covered physical exam, Medicare instructs us to subtract the usual fee for the covered service—the office visit or pelvic and breast exam—from the usual fee for the non-covered service—the physical exam—and bill the patient for the difference. Bill Medicare for the covered service, the pelvic and breast exam.

Here's how that looks:

Pelvic exam, preventive medicine exam:

G0101 Pelvic and breast exam
Q0091 Obtaining pap smear
99387 or 99397

How to bill this to the patient:
99397 $150
G0101   40   Bill to Medicare—subtract fee from patient balance
Q0091   25   Bill to Medicare—subtract fee from patient balance

Balance due from patient: $85

Related issues:

An ABN is required if you perform the G0101 and Q0091 at a greater time frequency than is allowed. Be sure to properly execute the ABN with specific reasons why you believe Medicare might not cover the service. Commercial payers will often pay the Q0091 code. The service described by G0101, however, is part of an age and gender appropriate physical exam. It would be incorrect to bill G0101 on the same day as you bill the preventive medicine services to commercial patients.

As part of the 2010 health care reform bill, Medicare will begin covering an annual wellness exam in 2011. The definition and requirements for this wellness exam are not known as this book goes to press.

Key points:

- These codes are diagnosis code specific. Using a general examination code will result in a denial.
- These codes have specific time limits.
- Obtain an ABN if either the diagnosis or the time limit code requirements are not met.
- Make sure to document seven of the 11 bullets for the pelvic and clinical breast exam.

See also: Preventive medicine services, preventive medicine services for Medicare patients, Advance Beneficiary Notice.

Citations:

CMS, http://www.cms.gov/PrevntionGenInfo

CMS, *Medicare Claims Processing Manual*, Pub 100-04, Chapter 18. http://www.cms.gov/Manuals/IOM/list.asp

Physician Quality Reporting Initiative (PQRI)

Definition:

The Physician Quality Reporting Initiative (PQRI) is a Medicare, pay-for-reporting system which provides an incentive payment for physicians and other eligible healthcare professionals who successfully report on quality indicators using Quality Data Codes (QDC) on claims for services provided to Medicare patients.

Explanation:

CMS is committed to transforming Medicare to value-based purchasing. In their Final Rule, in 2007, Medicare wrote: *"It is a top priority of CMS to transform Medicare from a passive payor to an active purchaser of high quality, efficient health care services. We are studying and implementing value-based purchasing initiatives for Medicare payment systems, including physician services."* Page 874 Final Rule, November 1, 2007. And again in the Medicare Physician Fee Schedule (MPFS) Calendar Year 2009 proposed rule, they said, *"The MPFS CY 2009 proposed rule continues an initiative of the Administration to transform the Medicare fee-for-service program into a prudent purchaser of health care services, paying for quality of care, not just quantity."* The Healthcare Reform Act of 2010 carries out this goal with numerous demonstration projects and continues the PQRI program.

Codes:

Each measure has its own Quality Data Codes that correspond to the CPT®/ICD 9 requirements of the measure.

Coverage: Medicare

Billing and coding:

PQRI started in the second half of 2007 with a potential bonus of 1.5% of Medicare charges and a payment cap calculation. Medicare allowed charges are the total allowance (not payment) submitted to Part B fee-for-service Medicare, excluding drugs and labs. Charges to Part A from Rural Health Centers and Federally Qualified Health Centers are not included.

In 2008, there were full and half year reporting options, with a possible 2% incentive payment, and no cap on the payment.

2009 saw Medicare split out E-prescribing as a stand alone incentive program and a separate, 2% incentive payment for successfully reporting in the PQRI program. Groups that participated in both and reported successfully for both were eligible for a 4% bonus on their total Medicare charges. In 2009, there were three ways to report: report on three measures 80% of the time, registry reporting, and measures group reporting. CMS is investigating reporting via electronic health records. There were full and half year period reporting options. Successful reporting is measured by National Provider Identifier (NPI) number, but the payment goes to the group. CMS reports show which doctors in a practice successfully reported. There is no requirement for all eligible professionals in a group to participate or for them to all use the same measures. The CMS website lists the eligible professionals who may participate in PQRI.

For 2010, there were numerous reporting options including reporting on individual measures or measures groups, full and half year reporting periods, and claims based, registry and large group methods to report. Ten measures could be reported using an electronic health record. The potential bonus in 2010 was 2%. For 2011, the bonus will be 1%, and in future years, there will be a penalty for not reporting. Like E-prescribing and using electronic health records, what started as a bonus becomes a penalty if the practice does not participate. The Health Care Reform Act of 2010) extends the bonus for PQRI until 2014. The penalty in 2015 for not reporting is that the group will be paid at 98.5% of the physician fee schedule amount. In 2016, a group not reporting will be paid at 98% of the fee schedule amount.

Specialty societies are a great source of information about the measures that work for a physician specialty. Looking at the list of measures (and printing it would use over a ream of paper) and measures groups can be overwhelming. Check your specialty society website first. Each year, a group needs to review the measures, because CMS adds and deletes measures each year. Reporting options and reporting periods vary, as well.

Common errors which kept groups from receiving a bonus, were:
- No NPI number on the claim
- Clearinghouse did not transmit line items with a 0 dollar value
- Quality Data Codes did not match the CPT®/ICD-9 codes for the measure

- Age limits on some measures meant Quality Data Codes were submitted on claims which did not meet the criteria of the measure
- Not reporting on a patient when covering for a partner lowered that physician's reporting percentage to less than 80%

Each measure has a specific set of criteria (the denominator, in CMS terms) which tells the provider what patient encounters should be reported. Some measures have specific CPT® and ICD-9 code combinations or are limited by age or gender and the number of times they are reported in the reporting period (once in the reporting period, or every time the service is provided.)

Related issues:

E-prescribing is a separate incentive program. The White House is also providing stimulus money for the use of electronic health records.

Medicare will begin publishing the names of physicians who successfully reported on a quality website in 2010. They will not publish the full results in 2010, although that cannot be far away, but only will publish whether a physician or other eligible professional successfully reported.

Key Points:

- All groups should review the measures each year and strongly consider participating in the program.
- CMS has provided a number of options for reporting, including claims based individual measures, claims based measures group, and registry reporting. They are investigating how data can be collected through an electronic health record.
- Carefully review the description of the measures selected.
- Some software companies are selling a product that will allow the practice to select which measures are being used, and will prompt the charge poster to enter one of the matching Quality Data Codes.

Citations:

www.cms.hhs.gov/PQRI

Pre-operative Exams

Definition:

Primary care providers and specialty providers are often asked to provide pre-operative clearance before a patient may go to surgery. These services are billed with E/M codes.

Explanation:

Medically necessary services prior to surgery are covered by Medicare and by many third party payers. What may and may not be billed after the decision for surgery is made but prior to surgery? It is necessary to review the CPT® and Medicare definitions for the global period. According to CMS, the global package for surgery includes a number of services as described below.

> The Medicare approved amount for these procedures includes payment for the following services related to the surgery when furnished by the physician who performs the surgery. The services included in the global surgical package may be furnished in any setting, e.g., in hospitals, ASCs, physicians' offices. Visits to a patient in an intensive care or critical care unit are also included if made by the surgeon. However, critical care services (99291 and 99292) are payable separately in some situations.
>
> - Pre-operative Visits—Pre-operative visits after the decision is made to operate beginning with the day before the day of surgery for major procedures and the day of surgery for minor procedures;
> - Intra-operative Services—Intra-operative services that are normally a usual and necessary part of a surgical procedure;
> - Complications Following Surgery—All additional medical or surgical services required of the surgeon during the post-operative period of the surgery because of complications which do not require additional trips to the operating room;
> - Post-operative Visits—Follow up visits during the post-operative period of the surgery that are related to recovery from the surgery;
> - Post-surgical Pain Management—By the surgeon;
> - Supplies—Except for those identified as exclusions; and
> - Miscellaneous Services—Items such as dressing changes; local incisional care; removal of operative pack; removal of cutaneous

sutures and staples, lines, wires, tubes, drains, casts, and splints; insertion, irrigation and removal of urinary catheters, routine peripheral intravenous lines, nasogastric and rectal tubes; and changes and removal of tracheostomy tubes.

CMS does not include this in the global period:

The initial consultation or evaluation of the problem by the surgeon to determine the need for surgery. Please note that this policy only applies to major surgical procedures. The initial evaluation is always included in the allowance for a minor surgical procedure;

Prior to 2010, pre-operative medical evaluations that met the criteria for consultations could be billed using consult codes for all payers. For commercial patients, whose insurances still recognize these codes, a physician may bill a pre-operative evaluation as a consult. For Medicare patients, and for patients with insurances that do not recognize consultation codes, bill for these evaluations with new or established patient codes in the office, with ED codes in the ED, and with initial hospital services codes for inpatients.

The CPT® book gives us a similar but not exactly the same definitions of a global surgical period. The CPT® book describes the global package as follows:

- For commercial payers, use the CPT® Definition:
- Local infiltration, metacarpal/metatarsal/digital block or local anesthesia
- Subsequent to the decision for surgery, one E/M encounter on the date immediately prior to or on the date of procedure (including history and physical)
- Immediate post-operative care, including dictating operative notes, talking with the family and other physicians
- Writing orders
- Evaluating the patient in the post-anesthesia recovery area
- Typical post-operative follow up care
- Surgical service includes surgical procedure and medical and surgical management of complications that do not require additional trips to the OR.
- Medically necessary return trips to the OR, without regard to fault, will be separately billed and paid for at a reduced rate. (Modifier 76 is for a repeat procedure by the same physician, modifier 77 is

for a repeat procedure by a different physician and modifier 78 is for a related procedure. See CPT® book for detailed description.)

- Global period includes follow up, typically for 90 days for major surgery. Commercial payers typically follow the global periods assigned by HCFA.
- The global period service and fee includes post-op care in and out of the hospital and: dressing changes, local incision care, removal of operative packs, staples, sutures, lines, wires, tubes, drains, casts, and splints, irrigation and removal of urinary catheters, routine IV lines, nasogastric and rectal tubes and changes and removal of tracheostomy tubes.
- Starred surgical procedures are typically minor procedures that are not paid using the global surgery policy. Most have a 0 or 10 day post op period.
- In general, insurance companies will not pay for a surgical procedure and an Evaluation and Management procedure on the same day. If there are two separately identifiable, significant services performed on the same day (and E/M and a procedure) and the documentation supports this, bill the E/M service with the -25 modifier.

Codes:

The E/M services are based on the type and place of service that was provided. Typically, these would be office visits or consultations in the 99201–99215 series or 99241–99245 series, or 99251–99255 series for a hospitalized patient. Starting January 1, 2010, Medicare no longer recognizes consultation codes.

Coverage:

Pre-operative clearance is provided by Medicare and other third party payers when it is medically necessary for the patient's care.

Billing and coding rules:

A primary care doctor may be paid to perform this pre-operative clearance if requested by the surgeon, and a specialist, such as a cardiologist or pulmonologist, may be asked for pre-operative clearance.

If a physician or NPP provides a medically necessary E/M service on the same day as a procedure with zero or 10 global days, use a 25 modifier on the procedure. If an E/M service is provided on the same day as a procedure with a 90 day global period and the visit is the one at which the decision for surgery was made, bill the E/M service with a 57 modifier.

Related issues:

Hospital or surgical center requirements for pre-operative visits do not fulfill Medicare's medical necessity criteria for payment. The pre-operative service must be indicated for that specific patient in order to be a covered service.

What about a surgeon who sees a patient and schedules the patient for surgery? Prior to the surgery, the hospital requires a pre-operative exam. The CPT® Assistant answered this question in May, 2009. If the physician has decided to perform a surgery, and the patient returns for a history and physical and to complete the pre-procedure paperwork, the service is not a separately reportable service and may not be billed.

E/M services prior to a screening colonoscopy are never paid by Medicare. A medically necessary E/M service is payable for diagnostic colonoscopy prior to the procedure.

Key points:

- A consult for a pre-operative clearance for payers that still pay for consults may only be billed if all of the requirements necessary for a consultation are met: a request from another healthcare professional, the rendering of an opinion, and a report returned to that healthcare professional.
- The correct diagnostic coding for pre-operative claims is as follows: The first diagnosis should be pre-operative screening in the V72.81 to V72.84 series of codes. The reason for the surgery is the second diagnosis used, and the patient's underlying medical conditions are the third and subsequent diagnosis codes used.
- The E/M visit at which the decision for surgery was made is paid with modifier 57 appended to the E/M service.

See also: Consultations, global surgical package, modifiers

Citation:

CMS, *Medicare Claims Processing Manual*, Pub 100-04, Chapter 12, Section 30.6.6 and Section 40, http://www.cms.gov/Manuals/IOM/list.asp

Preventive Medicine Services

Definition:

A preventive medicine service includes an age and gender appropriate history and exam, anticipatory guidance, risk factor reduction, provision of or referral for immunizations, and screening diagnostic tests.

Explanation:

Well visits, annual exams, physical exams—these are the words we use to describe the physician office component of preventive medicine services. These visits are defined as new and established patients, and separated by age groups. They include an age and gender appropriate comprehensive history and comprehensive exam. The CPT® book tells us that these comprehensive histories and exams are not the same as defined by the documentation guidelines. That is, the history does not require four items on the history of the present illness, ten systems reviewed, and all of the patient's past family, social, and medical history. Instead, the history is composed of a review of systems and past family, social, and medical history that is relevant to the patient's age and gender. For a child, this history will include developmental history. Similarly, the exam required is not the eight organ system comprehensive exam required for high level E/M codes.

The CPT® book suggests that clinicians consult their specialty societies, the U.S. Preventive Task Force, and the CDC for recommendations about what to include in these services, as well as what screening tests and immunizations to provide.

Codes: 99381–99397

Coverage:

Coverage for these services varies widely. Prior to the health care reform act, Medicare did not pay for routine services, but did pay for many screening services and some immunizations. As the book goes to press, Medicare is developing rules for the newly covered annual wellness exams. Rules for child health programs and Medicaid vary by state, but all Medicaid programs are required to provide a set of preventive services under their Early Periodic Screening, Diagnostic and Treatment (EPSDT) programs. Private coverage varies as well. Most HMO policies cover well care. Some PPO and indemnity plans have this coverage, as well. Unfortunately, it is difficult for any physician office to know based on the patient's identification card whether he or she has coverage for these services.

Billing and coding rules:

Most private pay policies allow annual billing of a preventive medicine service after the age of two. Prior to age two, babies and toddlers are seen more often. Follow the new patient rule to determine whether the patient is new or established, and then select the code based on the patient's age.

Include in the service an age and gender appropriate history and physical exam. Also, provide anticipatory guidance and risk factor reduction appropriate to the patient's age and gender. This includes recommendations for immunizations and screenings. These recommendations to patients are part of the definition of preventive medicine services. Clinicians may bill separately, however, for performing these screening tests. Also bill separately for the administration of immunizations and for the vaccine, if the vaccine was purchased by the practice.

Some practices want to bill separately for G0101, pelvic and breast exam, when billing for a code in the preventive medicine series. This is bundled into the preventive medicine codes for commercial patients. (Medicare rules are rules unto themselves and are discussed elsewhere in this book.)

The CPT® book includes two sets of immunization administration codes for vaccines. (Medicare uses HCPCS codes for administration that are discussed later). These codes are defined by the method of administration, whether or not the physician provided counseling about the vaccines, and the age of the patient. They are in the range 90465–90474.

Notice that these administration codes have a base code and an add-on code. The add-on code is an "each additional" code. That is, after billing the base code for the administration of the first vaccine, bill the add-on code for each additional vaccine, noting the number of additional administrations done in units. For example, if you administered three IM vaccines to a 12 year old, bill 90471, one unit, and 90472, with two units.

What about addressing a patient's medical problems on the same day as a preventive medicine service? Can a clinician be paid for two E/M services on the same day, the preventive medicine service and the office visit? According to the CPT® book, if a physician or NPP addresses an acute or chronic medical problem that requires significant extra work to perform key elements of the history, exam and medical decision making, the clinician can bill an office visit. The CPT® book tells us to bill an office visit with a 25 modifier on the same day as a preventive medicine service. This is correct coding, but is notoriously difficult to collect from third parties. Many Medicaid programs will only pay for one service in a day, and will select the lower paying code as the one to pay! Some commercial insurances will initially deny the office visit on the same day as a preventive medicine service. Some will pay on appeal, if the notes support that significant extra work was performed. Documenting the office visit in a separate note, distinct from the preventive medicine service will improve your chance of getting paid for both. However, billing staff should track their success in collecting for these services. Some practices find that they collect very little, but spend a significant amount of staff time. Clinicians do not like to ask patients to return for another visit, but often it is the only way to get paid for both services.

Related issues:

Diagnosis coding is critical in preventive medicine service, particularly for screening tests and immunizations. Using a generalized exam code, such as V70.0, can result in denials for screening tests and immunizations. Gynecologic offices use code V72.31 for well women exams.

Key points:

- Preventive medicine services include an age/gender appropriate history and exam, anticipatory guidance and risk factor reduction, referral for screening tests, and provision of immunizations.
- Coverage varies by commercial payers and policies.
- Bill for administration of vaccines and for the vaccine if the practice bought the serum.
- Coding rules allow a physician to bill for an office visit and a preventive medicine service on the same day, using a 25 modifier on the office visit. Do this when significant extra work was performed to diagnose or treat a patient's illness. Expect to have difficulty in getting paid for both on the same day.
- Be careful about diagnosis coding. Non-specific diagnosis coding may result in denials.

See also: New patients, pelvic and breast exam, preventive medicine for Medicare patients, welcome to Medicare

Citation:

Agency for Healthcare Research and Quality, http://www.ahrq.gov/clinic/uspstfix.htm (U.S. Preventive Task Force web site).

Preventive Medicine Services (Medicare)

Definition:

Medicare was developed for the care of sick and injured beneficiaries, and was not intended to cover preventive medicine services.

Explanation:

Over the years, Congress has passed many laws that pay for screening or preventive services. Annual physical exams were not covered by Medicare. However, the health care reform act of 2010 added in coverage for an annual wellness visit. As this book goes to press, CMS is developing the rules—and probably the new HCPCS codes—to describe that service. In addition, the health care reform act mandated that any preventive services which are rated with an A or B rating by the U.S. Preventive Task Force would be covered for Medicare beneficiaries. Medicare also pays for a "Welcome to Medicare" visit.

Codes:

99381–99397 for preventive medicine services are not covered.
G0402—Welcome to Medicare visit
Many HCPCS codes for covered screening services

The CMS website identifies these screening services as covered:
- "Welcome to Medicare" visit
- Adult immunization—influenza immunization, pneumococcal vaccination, hepatitis B vaccination
- Colorectal cancer screening
- Screening mammography
- Screening pap test and pelvic examination
- Prostate cancer screening
- Cardiovascular disease screening
- Diabetes screening
- Glaucoma screening
- Bone mass measurement
- Diabetes self-management, supplies, and services
- Medical nutrition therapy
- Smoking cessation

Coverage:

By Medicare statute. Covered screening services have gender, diagnosis and frequency limits.

Billing and coding rules:

As this book goes to press, CMS is developing the components of the annual wellness exam.

When billing for the covered screening and immunizations provided to Medicare patients, there are often HCPCS codes used in place of the CPT® codes. Review the chart in this entry, and download the updated version yearly. The diagnosis coding required for these services is specific.

Related issues:

The CMS web site provides a chart for download of covered preventive medicine services. This lists the specific CPT®, HCPCS and ICD-9 codes that are covered for Medicare patients and the frequency of coverage.

Key issues:

- Medicare does pay for many screening tests and immunizations. Use the specific HCPCS codes and diagnosis codes for those to prevent denial for these services.
- Watch the Medicare web site for updates to covered preventive services. The health care reform act of 2010 added an annual wellness exam. The draft of these services is described in the "Wellness Visits" entry.

See also: Preventive medicine services; "Welcome to Medicare" visit, pelvic and breast exam, wellness visits

Citations:

Medicare Claims Processing Manual, Pub 100-04, Chapter 18

http://www.cms.hhs.gov/PrevntionGenInfo/

Quick Reference Information: Medicare Preventive Services

Quick Reference Information: Medicare Preventive Services

SERVICE	HCPCS/CPT CODES	ICD-9-CM CODES	WHO IS COVERED	FREQUENCY	BENEFICIARY PAYS
Initial Preventive Physical Examination (IPPE) *Also known as the "Welcome to Medicare Physical Exam" or "Welcome to Medicare Visit"*	**Effective January 1, 2009** G0402 – IPPE G0403 – EKG for IPPE G0404 – EKG tracing for IPPE G0405 – EKG interpret & report *Important – Effective for dates of service on or after January 1, 2009, the screening EKG is an optional service that may be performed as a result of a referral from an IPPE*	No specific diagnosis code required for IPPE	All Medicare beneficiaries whose first Part B coverage began on or after January 1, 2005	**Once in a lifetime benefit per beneficiary** *Must be furnished no later than 12 months after the effective date of the first Medicare Part B coverage begins*	Copayment/coinsurance No deductible applies for code G0402, effective for dates of service on or after January 1, 2009 Deductible still applies for G0403, G0404, and G0405
Ultrasound Screening for Abdominal Aortic Aneurysm (AAA)	G0389 – Ultrasound exam AAA screen	No specific code *Contact local Medicare Contractor for guidance*	Medicare beneficiaries with certain risk factors for abdominal aortic aneurysm *Important – Eligible beneficiaries must receive a referral for an AAA ultrasound screening as a result of an IPPE*	**Once in a lifetime benefit per eligible beneficiary, effective January 1, 2007**	Copayment/coinsurance No deductible
Cardiovascular Disease Screenings	80061 – Lipid Panel 82465 – Cholesterol 83718 – Lipoprotein 84478 – Triglycerides	Report one or more of the following codes: V81.0, V81.1, V81.2	All asymptomatic Medicare beneficiaries *12-hour fast is required prior to testing*	**Every 5 years**	No copayment/coinsurance No deductible
Diabetes Screening Tests	82947 – Glucose, quantitative, blood (except reagent strip) 82950 – Glucose, post-glucose dose (includes glucose) 82951 – Glucose Tolerance Test (GTT), three specimens (includes glucose)	V77.1 *Report modifier "TS" (follow-up service) for diabetes screening where the beneficiary meets the definition of pre-diabetes*	Medicare beneficiaries with certain risk factors for diabetes or diagnosed with pre-diabetes *Beneficiaries previously diagnosed with diabetes are not eligible for this benefit*	• **2 screening tests per year for beneficiaries diagnosed with pre-diabetes** • **1 screening per year if previously tested, but not diagnosed with pre-diabetes or if never tested**	No copayment/coinsurance No deductible
Diabetes Self-Management Training (DSMT)	G0108 – DSMT, individual session, per 30 minutes G0109 – DSMT, group session (2 or more), per 30 minutes	No specific code *Contact local Medicare Contractor for guidance*	Medicare beneficiaries at risk for complications from diabetes, recently diagnosed with diabetes, or previously diagnosed with diabetes *Physician must certify that DSMT is needed*	• **Up to 10 hours of initial training within a continuous 12-month period** • **Subsequent years: Up to 2 hours of follow-up training each year after the initial year**	Copayment/coinsurance Deductible
Medical Nutrition Therapy (MNT)	97802, 97803, 97804, G0270, G0271 *Services must be provided by registered dietitian or nutrition professional*	*Contact local Medicare Contractor for guidance*	Medicare beneficiaries diagnosed with diabetes or a renal disease	**1st year: 3 hours of one-on-one counseling** **Subsequent years: 2 hours**	Copayment/coinsurance Deductible
Screening Pap Tests	G0123, G0124, G0141, G0143, G0144, G0145, G0147, G0148, P3000, P3001, Q0091	V76.2, V76.47, V76.49, V15.89, V72.31	All female Medicare beneficiaries	**Annually if high-risk, or childbearing age with abnormal Pap test within past 3 years** **Every 24 months for all other women**	Copayment/coinsurance for Pap test collection *(No copayment/coinsurance for Pap lab test)* No deductible
Screening Pelvic Exam	G0101 – Cervical or vaginal cancer screening; pelvic and clinical breast examination	V76.2, V76.47, V76.49, V15.89, V72.31	All female Medicare beneficiaries	**Annually if high-risk, or childbearing age with abnormal Pap test within past 3 years** **Every 24 months for all other women**	Copayment/coinsurance No deductible
Screening Mammography	77052, 77057, G0202	V76.11 or V76.12	All female Medicare beneficiaries age 40 or older	**Annually**	Copayment/coinsurance No deductible
Screening Mammography	77052, 77057, G0202	V76.11 or V76.12	Female Medicare beneficiaries ages 35 - 39	**One baseline**	Copayment/coinsurance No deductible
Bone Mass Measurements	G0130, 77078, 77079, 77080, 77081, 77083, 76977	*Contact local Medicare Contractor for guidance*	Medicare beneficiaries at risk for developing Osteoporosis	**Every 24 months** *More frequently if medically necessary*	Copayment/coinsurance Deductible

Quick Reference Information: Medicare Preventive Services

Quick Reference Information: Medicare Preventive Services

SERVICE	HCPCS/CPT CODES	ICD-9-CM CODES	WHO IS COVERED	FREQUENCY	BENEFICIARY PAYS
Colorectal Cancer Screening	G0104 – Flexible Sigmoidoscopy (high risk) G0105 – Colonoscopy (high risk) G0106 – Barium Enema (alternative to G0104) G0120 – Barium Enema (alternative to G0105) G0121 – Colonoscopy (not high risk) G0122 – Barium Enema (non-covered) G0328 – Fecal Occult Blood Test (alternative to 82270) 82270 – Fecal Occult Blood Test	Use appropriate code *Contact local Medicare Contractor for guidance*	• Medicare beneficiaries age 50 and older • Screening colonoscopy: Individuals at high risk; no minimum age requirement • No minimum age for having a barium enema as an alternative to a high risk screening colonoscopy if the beneficiary is at high risk	• Fecal Occult: Annually • Flexible Sigmoidoscopy: Every 4 years or once every 10 years after having a screening colonoscopy • Screening Colonoscopy: Every 24 months at high risk; every 10 years not at high risk • Barium Enema: Every 24 months at high risk; every 4 years not at high risk	No copayment/coinsurance or deductible for Fecal Occult Blood Tests For all other tests copayment/coinsurance apply No deductible
Prostate Cancer Screening	G0102 – Digital Rectal Exam (DRE)	V76.44	All male Medicare beneficiaries 50 or older (coverage begins the day after 50th birthday)	Annually	Copayment/coinsurance Deductible
Prostate Cancer Screening	G0103 – Prostate Specific Antigen Test (PSA)	V76.44	All male Medicare beneficiaries 50 or older (coverage begins the day after 50th birthday)	Annually	No copayment/coinsurance No deductible
Glaucoma Screening	G0117 – By an optometrist or ophthalmologist G0118 – Under the direct supervision of an optometrist or ophthalmologist	V80.1	Medicare beneficiaries with diabetes mellitus, family history of glaucoma, African-Americans age 50 and over, or Hispanic-Americans age 65 and over	Annually for beneficiaries in one of the high risk groups	Copayment/coinsurance Deductible
Seasonal Influenza Virus Vaccine	90655, 90656, 90657, 90658, 90660 – Influenza Virus Vaccine G0008 – Administration	V04.81 V06.6 – *When purpose of visit was to receive both seasonal influenza virus and pneumococcal vaccines*	All Medicare beneficiaries	Once per influenza season in the fall or winter *Medicare may provide additional flu shots if medically necessary*	No copayment/coinsurance No deductible
Pneumococcal Vaccine	90669 – Pneumococcal Conjugate Vaccine 90732 – Pneumococcal Polysaccharide Vaccine G0009 – Administration	V03.82 V06.6 – *When purpose of visit was to receive both pneumococcal and seasonal influenza virus vaccines*	All Medicare beneficiaries	Once in a lifetime *Medicare may provide additional vaccinations based on risk and provided that at least 5 years have passed since receipt of a previous dose*	No copayment/coinsurance No deductible
Hepatitis B (HBV) Vaccine	90740, 90743, 90744, 90746, 90747 – Hepatitis B Vaccine G0010 – Administration 90471 or 90472 – Administration (OPPS hospitals only)	V05.3	Medicare beneficiaries at medium to high risk	Scheduled dosages required	Copayment/coinsurance Deductible
Smoking and Tobacco-Use Cessation Counseling	99406 – counseling visit; intermediate, greater than 3 minutes up to 10 minutes 99407 – counseling visit; intensive, greater than 10 minutes	Use appropriate code *Contact local Medicare Contractor for guidance*	Medicare beneficiaries who use tobacco and have a disease or adverse health effect linked to tobacco use or take certain therapeutic agents whose metabolism or dosage is affected by tobacco use	2 cessation attempts per year; Each attempt includes maximum of 4 intermediate or intensive sessions; up to 8 sessions in a 12-month period	Copayment/coinsurance Deductible

Prolonged Services

Definition:

Prolonged services are defined as Evaluation and Management services which take the provider 30 minutes more than the typical time for that code. Prolonged services codes are add-on codes to specific E/M services.

Explanation:

Many E/M services have typical times established for each code. These are listed in the CPT® book and include new patient visits, established patient visits, initial hospital services, subsequent hospital services, nursing facility services and consults. There is no time established for observation services, emergency department visits or most preventive medicine services.

Physicians and NPPs may use the add-on codes with specific E/M codes to indicate that the time spent exceeded the typical time for that code by 30 minutes or more.

There are two sets of codes. The first is for direct face-to-face contact, and it is typically a paid service by third party payers. The second set of prolonged services codes is used to indicate that a prolonged service was provided without a face-to-face service. Payers generally do not cover these codes.

Codes:

99354–99357 for prolonged services with face-to-face contact
99358–99359 for prolonged services without face-to-face contact with
   the patient

Coverage:

Prolonged service codes are typically covered for face-to-face services, but not for non-face-to-face services.

Billing and coding rules:

Never bill these codes alone. Always add them on to the appropriate E/M services when you submit your claim. The time provided does not need to be continuous, but only provider time counts. A practice may not bill for staff time under prolonged services codes.

For example, a patient with asthma presents to the practice with wheezing and shortness of breath. The physician orders a nebulizer treatment, and the patient is in the office treatment room for

		Prolonged Services Code	
Code	**Typical time for code**	**Threshold time to bill 99356**	**Threshold time to bill codes 99356 & 99357**
Initial hospital services			
99221	30	60	105
99222	50	80	125
99223	70	100	145
Subsequent hospital visits			
99231	15	45	90
99232	25	55	100
99233	35	65	110
Inpatient consults			
99251	20	50	95
99252	40	70	115
99253	55	85	130
99254	80	110	155
99255	110	140	185
Nursing Home services—initial			
99304	25	55	100
99305	35	65	110
99306	45	75	120
Nursing home services—subsequent			
99307	10	40	85
99308	15	45	90
99309	25	55	100
99310	35	65	110
Nursing home services—annual			
99318	30	60	105

60 minutes. A staff member is with the patient for all of that time. The physician, however, spent 10 minutes with the patient in doing an assessment and ordering the treatment, and has checked on the patient twice during the hour. The total physician time is 20 minutes. In this case, it is incorrect to bill a prolonged services code.

Document provider time in the medical record. "I spent a total of 60 minutes with the patient in face-to-face service today." (See Prolonged Services Code Chart, above.) Medicare requires start and stop times, not simply a statement of the total time.

CMS Transmittal 1490, CR 5972, April 11, 2008:

What about visits that are entirely counseling, for which no history and exam are documented? This might be the case in a situation when a patient returns to talk about a known diagnosis and the treatment options. Medicare says that if the visit is entirely counseling, use the highest level code in that category of code before using prolonged services. For example, a patient returns to an oncologist to discuss the treatment options for breast cancer, and the entire visit is spent in that discussion. The visit category is established patient visit, and the total face-to-face visit time was 80 minutes. First, look at the typical time for the highest code in that category, 99215. It is 40 minutes. Then, look at the chart to see what the threshold time is to bill the prolonged services code. It is 70 minutes, or 30 minutes more than the typical time. In this case, bill 99215 and 99354.

Can prolonged services be used for a second hospital visit on the same day, by the same physician or that physician's same-specialty partner? Yes, in rare circumstances. The initial visit must have the typical time documented. The second visit must have the time documented as well. For Medicare, the second visit, on which the prolonged services code is based, must be for face-to-face, not unit, time and must be documented with the start and stop time. Most prolonged hospital services take place on the unit, but not necessarily the bedside. The Medicare rules are more stringent than CPT® rules in requiring the prolonged service to be exclusively face-to-face with the patient.

Related issues:

Match the prolonged services codes with the E/M service for which they are covered. Prolonged services are add-on codes. Never bill an add-on code on its own.

Key points:

- Document the total provider time in the medical record; Medicare requires start and stop times.
- Document the medical necessity for the additional time in providing the services. Why did it take so long to see this patient?
- Use these with their companion E/M code and not for procedures or for any other E/M codes.

See also: Time based codes.

Citation:

CMS, *Medicare Claims Processing Manual*, Pub 100–04, Chapter 12, Section 30.6.15, http://www.cms.gov/Manuals/IOM/list.asp

Recovery Audit Contractor Initiative

Definition:

The Recovery Audit Contractor (RAC) Initiative started as a demonstration project in three states. The goal was to recover money incorrectly paid by Medicare. CMS hired private contractors, paying them on a contingency basis. Congress passed the Tax Relief and Health Care Act of 2006, making the program permanent and expanding it over time to all states by 2010.

Explanation:

RAC is a post payment review. Each private RAC contractor uses its own proprietary software to review paid claims data and select records for review. The initial demonstration project focused heavily on hospital services and durable medical equipment. Because the RACs are paid on a percentage of money returned to the Medicare trust fund, they focused on higher value services.

Codes: All

Coverage: Medicare fee for service payments.

Billing and coding rules:

The RAC contractors use the same rules as your Medicare Administrative Contractor (MAC) in determining whether a payment is correct, including National Coverage Determinations, Local Coverage Determinations and Medicare manuals. There are two types of reviews: automated, for which no medical record review is required, and manual, which requires reviewing medical records. Prior to implementing any work, the RAC must seek approval from CMS for issues to review and post the issues on their website.

The look back period is three years, and no claims can be reviewed for services prior to October1, 2007. CMS has limited the number of records that an RAC may request.

Key points:

- A robust compliance program is a practice's best protection against an RAC audit.
- Coding education is essential.

- The RAC for each geographical area is listed on CMS's website. Review the issues that are the RAC's agenda.
- If a practice receives a request from the RAC for notes, carefully review all documents that are sent, but do respond to the request.
- If a practice disagrees with an RAC determination, there is an appeal process.
- It is prudent to contact a lawyer.

See also: Health Care Reform Act.

Citations:

www.cms.gov/RAC

Reciprocal Billing Arrangements

Definition:

Medicare rules allow a patient's regular physician to submit a claim for services provided by a substitute covering physician on an occasional reciprocal basis.

Explanation:

Some physicians have coverage arrangements for care of their patients when they are not available, such as on weekends or during vacations. Many of these covering physicians bill directly for the services they provide to patients. However, Medicare has a provision for the regular physician to bill for the covering substitute physician *as if* the regular physician had provided that service. This is called reciprocal billing.

Codes:

The Q5 modifier is attached to the procedure code to indicate that the services were provided under a reciprocal billing arrangement.

Coverage: This is a Medicare rule.

Billing and coding rules:

The patient's regular physician may bill and collect for services provided by a substitute physician if the regular physician is unavailable when the patient seeks services from him or her. The maximum time period for which the substitute physician may provide services and the regular physician may bill under the reciprocal billing arrangement is 60 continuous days, measured from the first day the substitute physician begins seeing patients. If the regular physician is away for more than 60 days, the regular physician may not bill Medicare for the services provided by the covering physician. This time period is continuous, even if the substitute physician sees and bills no patients on some days. If the regular physician returns to work and then take a subsequent vacation, a new period of coverage begins with the new time taken off.

A physician may have reciprocal verbal or written arrangements with more than one physician.

The regular physician must indicate in field 24D on the CMS form 1500 that the service was provided by a substitute physician. This is indicated by appending modifier Q5 to the procedure code. As this book is being prepared, CMS is issuing instructions for completion of the updated form 1500. Practices that use reciprocal billing should ask their carriers if the provider number of the covering physician needs to be indicated on the form. The regular physician must keep a record of the services provided by the substitute physician. The regular physician's provider ID number is entered in block 24K of the line item.

Follow up coverage during the global post up period by a substitute physician does not need to be reported in any way during claims submission.

For hospice patients, claims submitted by the designated attending physician but provided by another group member also require the Q5 modifier on the procedure code in item 24.

Related issues:

The regular physician, in submitting claims for the substitute physician, is taking responsibility for the claim.

Key points:

- Reciprocal billing is a Medicare rule.
- Check with your third party payer before using reciprocal billing for any of their patients.
- This allows the regular physician to bill for services provided by a substitute physician when the regular physician is unavailable, and the patient seeks care. The physician can have multiple arrangements with physicians, and these do not need to be in writing.
- The maximum time period for substitute physician services billing under the reciprocal billing arrangement is sixty continuous days. Days count even when there are some days in which the subsequent physician does not provide services.
- Append the Q5 modifier on the procedure code. This indicates that the services are being billed under a reciprocal billing arrangement.
- The regular physician must keep a record of services provided by the substitute physician.

See also: Locum tenens billing.

Citation:

CMS, *Medicare Claims Processing Manual*, Pub 100-04, Chapter 1, section 30.2.10, http://www.cms.gov/Manuals/IOM/list.asp

Reviewing Medical Records

Definition:

Physicians and NPPs routinely review voluminous medical records for new and established patients.

Explanation:

The care of a patient requires both primary care and specialty clinicians to review prior medical records. This review can take twenty minutes, thirty minutes, or more. Documenting the information discovered in this review counts in the calculation of the amount of data reviewed for medical decision-making for an E/M service and may—but does not always—increase the level of medical decision-making when deciding on the level of service.

Codes: None.

Coverage: None.

Billing and coding rules:

Reviewing medical records is part of the preparatory and follow up work of a paid medical service, but payers do not reimburse separately for this service. Reviewing medical records and documenting the information found there is one of the data points considered in the amount of data reviewed for an evaluation and management service. Here is what the documentation guidelines say about that.

> DG: Relevant findings from the review of old records, and/or the receipt of additional history from the family, caretaker or other source to supplement that obtained from the patient should be documented. If there is no relevant information beyond that already obtained, that fact should be documented. A notation of "Old records reviewed" or "additional history obtained from family" without elaboration is insufficient.

The widely used Marshfield Clinic audit sheet for selection assigns two data points for this review. Not all carriers follow that guideline. With other data, this sometimes results in a higher level of medical decision-making. Medical decision-making is only one of the three key components in selecting an E/M service, so a higher level of medical decision-making might result in a higher E/M code.

Related issues:

Physicians and NPPs perform many non-reimbursable services in the course of their day. Reviewing prior medical records is one of these. CMS considers this work part of the pre- and post work for a billable service.

Key points:

- Payers do not offer separate reimbursement for reviewing old medical records.
- Time spent before or after the visit may not be included in the time of the visit, if time is used to select the E/M code in the office.
- Document what additional information was obtained from the old record.
- This data review may result in a higher level of medical decision making for an E/M code.

See also: Telephone calls, care plan oversight, care plan oversight for Medicare patients, time based codes.

Citation:

CMS Documentation Guidelines,
http://www.cms.hhs.gov/MLNEdWebGuide/25_EMDOC.asp

Shared Visits (Medicare)

Definition:
Shared visits are E/M services which are shared or split between a physician and a qualified NPP in the hospital.

Explanation:
If a physician and an NPP each provide part of an E/M service in the hospital (inpatient/outpatient/ED), the visit may be billed as a shared visit, using the physician provider number. This allows the practice to bill for the service under the physician provider number and be paid for the service at 100% of the physician fee schedule. (Shared services done in the physician's office must meet incident to rules.)

Codes: E/M codes.

Coverage: These are Medicare rules.

Billing and coding rules:
In a shared visit, both the physician and the NPP have a face-to-face service with the patient, and both document their part of the visit in the medical record. The physician must see the patient and document some clinically relevant portion of the note. This does not need to be extensive or repetitive, but must be more explicit than, "Seen and agree." The physician note, which is typically less extensive than the NPP note, should show that the physician saw the patient and participated in the care in a meaningful way. For example, the physician might note, "Saw patient. Agree with Mr. Scully's plan. We'll follow her labs again tomorrow and hopefully can discharge her." Or, "Saw patient. Agree with Mr. Scully's history and plan. Her lungs sound clearer to me and she reports that she has less shortness of breath at night."

If the documentation shows that both the physician and NPP had face-to-face services with the patient, and both have documented something of clinical relevance, bill the service under the physician's provider number. Add together the documentation elements from both notes to select the level of service. If the physician did not see the patient, but provided supervision or advice to the NPP, bill the service under the NPP provider number. NPPs are paid at 85% of the physician fee schedule.

Because shared visits in the office must meet the incident to guidelines, shared visits may only be billed for established patient visits in the office. If the visit meets the incident to guidelines, it may be billed under the physician provider number whether or not the physician saw the patient and provided part of the care.

Related issues:

Groups with a large number of inpatients often use NPPs as a way of managing their care. The physician can spend part of the day in the hospital, but return to the office to see patients there for most of the day. The NPP stays at the hospital, writes the longer notes, and does the management the rest of the day. This not only saves the physician time in documentation, but keeps them from the interruption of repeated phone calls with lab results, requests for new orders, etc. Many practices find this an effective way to manage patients.

Key points:

- Both the physician and the NPP must document a face-to-face service with the patient.
- The physician must document a clinically relevant portion of the history, exam or medical decision making. Writing something like "Seen and agree" is insufficient.
- Shared visits are allowed for inpatients, ED visits, and in the outpatient department. Shared visits are only allowed in the office if they meet incident to requirements.
- Bill shared visits under the physician provider number and combine the documentation from both providers to select the level of service.

See also: Incident to services.

Citations:

CMS, *Medicare Claims Processing Manual*, Pub. 100-04, Chapter 12, Section 30.6.1, http://www.cms.gov/Manuals/IOM/list.asp

CMS, Transmittal 782, Change Request 4125.

Smoking Cessation Counseling

Definition:

Medicare now covers counseling to help patients stop smoking if they have a disease or an adverse health effect from tobacco use, or if they are taking a medication which is adversely effected by the tobacco use.

Explanation:

Smoking related illnesses account for significant preventable morbidity and death. In 2005, Medicare added the counseling benefit to address tobacco use among patients with adverse health effects.

Codes:

99406 Smoking and tobacco use cessation counseling visit; intermediate, greater than three minutes up to 10 minutes.

99407 Smoking and tobacco use cessation counseling visit; intensive up to 10 minutes.

Coverage:

There is a Medicare benefit with frequency limits. Many commercial payers cover the service as well.

Billing and coding rules:

The smoking cessation service may be provided on the same day as an E/M service as long as there are two significant, separately identifiable services provided. For example, a clinician might treat a patient's diabetes and chronic obstructive pulmonary disease and provide smoking cessation counseling at the same visit. Append modifier 25 to the E/M service.

Medicare will cover eight sessions in a 12 month period. After one year has elapsed, another eight sessions are allowed for the beneficiary. Keep in mind that this is not a service that is allowed eight times per provider, but eight times per patient by any provider.

The diagnosis code submitted with the claim should reflect the patient's condition that is adversely affected by tobacco use. Use also 305.1. Smoking cessation services that take less than three minutes are part of the E/M service and are not separately billable. Deductibles and co-insurance apply.

Whenever time is used to select a CPT® code or an HCPCS code, time must be documented in the medical record. Document the time spent in smoking cessation counseling.

Providers will need to know how many smoking cessation sessions a beneficiary has received prior to providing the service. Medicare has giver providers access to their Common Working File (CWF). Using the patient's health information number, a provider may view the number of sessions a patient has received. Medicare allows the patient eight sessions in the first year that the service is provided, and then after a break of a year, another eight sessions.

Related issues:

An ABN will be required if the physician provides the service more frequently than is allowed by Medicare. An ABN will also be needed if multiple physicians are providing the service to one patient and they have surpassed the number of services that the patient is allowed.

Key points:

- Remember to document time in the medical record when providing smoking cessation.
- Use the diagnosis code related to the patient's illness for which the smoking cessation counseling is provided.
- Check the Common Working File for your beneficiary to see if the beneficiary has already received the maximum services allowed for the time period.

See also: Time based codes.

Citation:

CMS, *Medicare Claims Processing Manual*, Pub 100-04, Chapter 32, Section 12, http://www.cms.gov/Manuals/IOM/list.asp

Teaching Physician Rules Based on Time

Definition:

The teaching physician rules for CPT® codes based on time allow an organization to bill only for the time spent and documented by the attending physician, not the resident. The terms "attending physician" and "teaching physician" are used interchangeably in this entry.

Explanation:

Procedure codes determined on the basis of time are billable in a teaching physician setting based solely on the time spent and documented by the attending physician. Although the resident may see the patient with the teaching physician before or after the teaching physician service, only the time spent by the attending physicians counts in code selection.

Codes:

Following are the codes from the *Medicare Claims Processing Manual*, which are based on time.

- Individual medical psychotherapy (HCPCS codes 90804–90829)
- Critical care services (CPT® codes 99291–99292)
- Hospital discharge day management (CPT® codes 99238–99239)
- E/M codes in which counseling and/or coordination of care dominates (more than 50 percent) of the encounter, and time is considered the key or controlling factor to qualify for a particular level of E/M service
- Prolonged services (CPT® codes 99354–99359)
- Care plan oversight (HCPCS codes G0181–G0182).

Coverage: Teaching physician rules are Medicare rules.

Billing and coding rules:

For psychiatric time based codes, the requirement for the attending physician, not the psychologist, may be met by concurrent observation of the service by use of one way mirror or video equipment. Audio equipment does not meet the requirement.

For all other services, the attending physician must personally document the time he or she spends providing the care.

For E/M codes based on time, the attending physician should document the total time of the visit, note that the visit was more than 50% counseling, and describe the nature of the counseling.

Related issues:

Time based codes require time to be documented in the medical record, not just the billing record.

A resident is defined by Medicare as a physician enrolled in an approved graduate medical education program. Append modifier GC to these services.

Key points:

- To use a time based code, the attending physician must personally be present for the time of the service provided.
- The attending physician must personally document in the medical record the time spent providing the service.
- Use modifier GC on claims for teaching physician services. This modifier does not affect payment but tells the carrier that these were services performed using the teaching physician rules.

See also: Teaching physician rules for critical care, teaching physician rules for procedures, teaching physician E/M services, teaching physician rules for medical students, time based codes, critical care.

Citations:

CMS, *Medicare Claims Processing Manual*, Pub. 100-04, Chapter 12, Section 100, http://www.cms.gov/Manuals/IOM/list.asp

Teaching Physician Rules for Critical Care Services

Definition:

These rules govern the provision of critical care services in a teaching institution when those service are billed by an attending physician, and a resident has participated in the patient's care. The terms "attending physician" and "teaching physician" are used interchangeably in this entry.

Explanation:

In a teaching facility, attending physicians, fellows, residents, and medical students all participate in the care of a patient. Medicare has specific rules and policies describing which services must be personally performed and documented by the attending physician in order to bill for the services under the attending physician's name.

Critical care codes are time-based codes. Since only an attending physician can bill for care provided to a critically ill patient, the time must be documented in the medical record by the attending physician.

Codes: 99291–99292.

Coverage: These are Medicare rules.

Billing and coding rules:

Only count the attending physician's critical care time. The attending physician must personally document all of the requirements for critical care. Documentation should state that the patient is critically ill, that the attending physician provided critical care treatment to that patient, and how much time the attending physician spent in providing care. The resident's note will supplement this entry about the patient's condition and treatment, but the resident physician's time can not be counted in critical care billing. It would be insufficient to write "Seen and agree" by the attending physician with the resident's note.

Apply modifier GC to the critical care code.

Related issues:

Review the requirements for critical care billing. The patient must be critically ill, critical care services must be provided to the patient, and time must be documented in the medical records.

Medicare continues to use the word "unstable" to define critical care services even though this has been removed from the CPT® definition. Document the patient's status clearly. Performing procedures and other E/M services have their own specific teaching physician rules. Review those if you are providing other services.

Key points:

- The attending physician must provide critical care services to the patient and document that the time spent providing critical care was 30 minutes or more in order to meet the threshold to bill 99291.
- The attending physician must legibly sign the critical care note.
- It should be clear what service the attending physician provided.
- Time spent in teaching does not count as critical care time billable to Medicare.
- Apply the GC modifier to services provided under the teaching physician rules.

See also: Teaching physician rules for E/M services, teaching physician rules—primary care exception, teaching physician rules for surgical procedures, procedures, teaching physician rules for medical students, teaching physician rules for time based care, critical care.

Citations:

CMS, *Medicare Claims Processing Manual*, Pub 100-04, Chapter 12, Section 100, http://www.cms.gov/Manuals/IOM/list.asp

Teaching Physician Rules for Evaluation and Management Codes

Definition:

There are a specific set of rules for the attending physician to comply with in order to bill for Evaluation and Management (E/M) services provided partly by a resident and partly by the attending physician. These are explained by CMS in the Teaching Physician Rules. The terms "attending physician" and "teaching physician" are used interchangeably in this entry.

Explanation:

The teaching physician rules for the supervision of residents define a resident as an intern, resident, or fellow enrolled in an accredited graduate medical education program. A medical student is never considered to be a resident. An attending physician may bill for the services provided jointly with a resident if the attending physician sees the patient, performs a critical or key portion of the E/M service, and participates in the patient's management. The attending physician may see the patient jointly with the resident and be physically present for the entire session, or may see the patient at a different time from the resident physician. Their services may partially overlap with the resident or may be performed at a different time on the same calendar date.

The attending physician must personally document his or her participation in the patient's care and link his or her work with the resident note, following specific Medicare guidelines.

Codes: E/M services.

Coverage: Medicare, and other payers.

Billing and coding rules:

The first requirement for the attending physician to bill for an E/M service done jointly with a resident physician is that the attending physician must see the patient on the same calendar date. The attending physician must participate in the care of the patient by performing the key elements/critical portions of the E/M service, and then documenting the service in a way that links the attending physician's note and the resident's note.

Evaluation and Management services have three key components: history, exam, and medical decision making. Some of these codes require all three key components to meet the level of service being billed. Others require just two of the three components. The teaching physician rules require the attending physician to document something from all three components for the first set of codes and something from two of the three key components from the second set of rules.

The attending physician must have a face-to-face contact with the patient in order to bill for the service.

E/M services requiring three of three key components: Initial hospital and services; ED visits, new patient visits, and consults

For these services, the attending physician must see the patient and write a summary note linking his or her note to the resident's note. This note must confirm or revise the resident's findings. The attending physician should document a clinically relevant portion of the history, exam, and medical decision making. For example, for an admission, the attending physician might write, "I saw and examined the patient. Her history is significant for multiple previous episodes of SOB. Her breathing today is unlabored, with normal breath sounds throughout. I agree with Dr. Resident's plan for consult to the pulmonary specialist."

This note confirms that the attending physician saw and examined the patient, participated in the care, and supervised the resident. If properly linked in this way, the level of service is determined by both of the notes of the attending physician and the resident.

E/M services requiring two of three of the key components: subsequent hospital visits and established patient visits

For these services, the attending physician must document two of the three elements of history, exam, and medical decision making.

Seeing the patient, performing a critical or key component of the service, and participating in the plan of care must be documented personally by the attending physician. The attending physician must also sign the note.

Here are other examples of linking statements that meet the criteria:

- For initial hospital services: "I performed a history and physical examination of the patient and discussed his management with the resident. I reviewed Dr. Resident's note and agree with the documented findings and plan of care. I would consider increasing his dosage of lasix."

- For a subsequent hospital visit: "Day three. I saw and evaluated the patient. I agree with the assessment and plan as documented in Dr. Cardiology Resident's note."
- For a subsequent hospital visit: "Internal medicine attending note: I saw and examined the patient. I agree with the resident's note. The heart murmur is louder, so I suggest that we consult Cardiology for a possible echo."
- Initial hospital service or subsequent care: "I was present with Dr. Resident during the entire history and exam. We discussed the case and I agree with the findings and plan as documented in Dr. Resident's note."
- Subsequent care: "I saw the patient with the resident and agree with Dr. Resident's findings and plan."
- Initial or follow-up visit: "I saw and evaluated the patient. Discussed with Dr. Resident and agree with the findings and plan as documented in Dr. Resident's note."

Here are examples of attending physician statements that do not meet the criteria: "Seen and agree" and "Agree with resident's note."

Related issues:

Services provided under the primary care exception rule have different requirements.

Medical students are not considered residents and their services may not be billed by the attending physician. Medical students may only document a review of systems and the family medical-social history for an evaluation and management service.

NPP students, that is nurse practitioner students or physicians assistant students, are not considered residents, and the services for these students may not be billed by an attending physician or an NPP.

Whether the attending physician needs to document history, exam, or both, as well as the medical decision making, depends on the Documentation Guideline requirement for that code. Some E/M codes require two of three key components and some require all three. For those that require three, the attending physician must document from each of the three.

Append modifier GC to these services.

Key points:

- The attending physician must document that the patient was seen that day, the key or critical portions of the history and/or exam, and the physician's participation in the patient's care through medical decision making.
- The Medicare claims processing manual specifically states that entries such as "seen and agree" or "seen with a resident and agree with above note" are insufficient. The documentation must reference the resident's note, show physical presence of the attending physician, document the key or critical portions of the history and/or the exam, and show involvement in the patient's care.
- The attending physician does not need to repeat an entire portion of the note in order to bill for the service.
- The resident may not document the attending physician's presence or participation for E/M services.
- The attending physician must document his or her own participation.
- Append modifier GC to these services.

See also: Teaching physician rules for E/M services, teaching physician rules for a primary care exception, teaching physician rules on procedures, teaching physician rules for medical students, teaching physician rules for time based care, critical care.

Citations:

CMS, *Medicare Claims Processing Manual*, Pub 100-04, Chapter 12, Section 100, http://www.cms.gov/Manuals/IOM/list.asp

Teaching Physician Rules for Medical Students

Definition:

Medical students are not residents, and their services may not be billed using the teaching physician rules. NPP student services are not payable by Medicare under the teaching physician rules. The terms "attending physician" and "teaching physician" are used interchangeably in this entry.

Explanation:

Medicare has developed specific rules for documenting and reimbursing teaching physician services. Medical students are not defined as residents and may not be billed using these rules.

Codes: All.

Coverage: These are Medicare rules but are followed by other payers.

Billing and coding rules:

For an E/M service, a medical student may only document a review of systems and the medical, family, and social history. The attending physician or resident must perform and document all other portions of the E/M service, including the chief complaint, history of present illness, exam, assessment, and care plan. If a medical student documents a review of systems and the family medical history, the attending physician should indicate that he or she has reviewed this information.

A procedure performed by a medical student may not be billed.

Related issues:

For an Evaluation and Management service, a medical student may only document what another staff person in the physician office can document: a review of systems and the family/medical/social history. NPP student services are not payable. It is insufficient to countersign a note by a student and write "seen and agreed."

Key points:

- Medical students and NPP students may only document reviews of systems and past medical/family/social histories.
- Medical student services are not covered by the teaching physician rules.

See also: Teaching physician rules for E/M services, teaching physician rules for primary care exceptions, teaching physician rules for surgical procedures, teaching physician rules for time based care.

Citations:

CMS, *Medicare Claims Processing Manual*, Pub 100-04, Chapter 12, Section 100, http://www.cms.gov/Manuals/IOM/list.asp

CMS, http://www.cms.gov/MLNEdWebGuide/25_EMDOC.asp

AAMC, http://www.aamc.org/advocacy/library/teachphys/medicareqa121603.pdf

Teaching Physician Rules for Primary Care Exception

Definition:

The teaching physician rules allow carriers to pay for physician claims furnished by residents without the presence of an attending physician when the services meet the requirements for the primary care exception. The terms "attending physician" and "teaching physician" are used interchangeably in this entry.

Explanation:

Graduate medical education (GME) programs that plan to use the primary care exception billing rules must attest in writing, and keep in their own files, a statement that all of the requirements are being met. The services must be furnished in the outpatient department of a hospital or other ambulatory care center in which the time spent by residents are included in determining direct GME payments to the hospital by the fiscal intermediary.

The resident must have completed more than six months of residency in order to provide these services without the presence of an attending physician.

Codes: 99201–99203 and 99211–99213 and "Welcome to Medicare" visit.

Coverage: Medicare.

Billing and coding rules:

The teaching physician may supervise up to four residents at any one time. During the time of the supervision, the teaching physician may not have any other responsibilities; must assume responsibility for those patients seen by the residents; must ensure that appropriate services are rendered; must review the history, exam, diagnosis, and plan with each resident during or immediately after each visit; and must document the extent of the review and care plan in the services furnished to each beneficiary.

The patients must consider the center to be their continuing source of healthcare. Residents must generally follow the same group of patients during their residency.

Residents may provide typical primary care services of acute or chronic problems. The *Medicare Claims Processing Manual* states that family practice, general internal medicine, geriatric medicine, pediatrics, and obstetrics/gynecology are the specialties most likely to qualify for the primary care exception.

Bill for these services with modifier GE.

Key points:

- Organizations need to keep records on file showing that they qualify for the primary care exception. These do not need to be submitted to their fiscal intermediary or carrier, and pre-approval is not needed.
- An attending physician may supervise up to four residents at a time.
- The resident must have completed six months of an approved GME program in order to be eligible to bill under this rule.
- There are seven E/M codes that can be billed using this rule.
- The attending physician must document his or her supervision of the resident's care of the patient.
- Append modifier GE on claims submitted using the teaching physician rules.

See also: Teaching physician rules for E/M services, teaching physician rules procedures, teaching physician rules for medical students, teaching physician rules for time based care.

Citations:

CMS, *Medicare Claims Processing Manual*, Pub 100-04, Chapter 12, Section 100, http://www.cms.gov/Manuals/IOM/list.asp

Teaching Physician Rules for Surgical Procedures

Definition:

The teaching physician rules for Medicare have specific rules regarding the performance of procedures by residents in order for the attending physician to bill for the service under their own provider number.

Explanation:

The teaching physician rules for Medicare require that the attending physician be present for the entire procedure for minor surgeries that take less than five minutes. For major procedures, the attending physician must be physically present for the critical or key portions of the procedure and must be immediately available to provide assistance during the remainder of the procedure. For endoscopy, the attending physician must be present from the introduction of the scope until its withdrawal. The terms "attending physician" and "teaching physician" are used interchangeably in this entry.

Codes: Surgical procedures.

Coverage: Medicare.

Billing and coding rules:

The attending physician must personally document his or her presence during the procedure. Without the presence of the attending physician and the appropriate statement linking the attending physician's note with the resident's note, the organization may not bill for this service.

The teaching physician is responsible for the pre-operative, operative and post-operative care, although the teaching physician may decide which post-operative visits require his or her presence.

An example of an attending physician statement which links to the resident note is "I was present for the entire minor procedure or endoscopy," or "I was present for the critical key portions of the procedure and immediately available for the remainder of the procedure. These key portions were . . ." Being immediately available to help means being on the unit within the suite of rooms and not separated by an elevator or stairwell.

Minor procedures of less than five minutes duration require that the attending physician be present for the entire procedure.

For endoscopies, the attending physician must be personally present in the room for the entire viewing from when the scope is introduced until the scope is withdrawn. Viewing from a monitor is insufficient to allow the attending physician to bill for the endoscopy performed by a resident.

For major procedures, the attending physician must be physically present for the critical/key portions of the surgical procedure and must be immediately available to provide assistance during the entire procedure. The attending physician need not be present for the opening or closing, unless those portions of the surgery are critical for that patient. For overlapping surgeries, the teaching physician must be present for the critical portions of each surgery. In addition, the teaching physician must personally document the key portions of both procedures. If the teaching physician leaves the operating room after key portions of the procedure to start another procedure, another physician must be available to intervene in the first case, should that be necessary. A resident does not qualify as a physician for this purpose. Indicate the name of the second surgeon in the note. If an attending physician is involved in supervising three overlapping surgeries, the attending physician may not bill for these concurrent surgical procedures.

Append modifier GC to these services.

Related issues:

Teaching physician rules vary by the type of service performed: procedures, E/M services, and time-based services. This is a high-risk area with significant fines and penalties for non-compliance.

Key points:

- The attending physician's presence during a procedure is required to bill for the procedure.
- The extent of that presence varies according to the type of surgery being performed.
- Attending physicians must personally document their presence.
- Procedures performed by a medical student or an NPP student are not billable services.
- Append modifier GC to these services.

See also: Teaching physician rules for E/M services, teaching physician rules for primary care, teaching physician rules for critical care, teaching physician rules for medical students, teaching physician rules for time based codes.

Citations:

CMS, *Medicare Claims Processing Manual*, Pub 100-04, Chapter 12, Section 100, http://www.cms.gov/Manuals/IOM/list.asp

Telephone Calls

Definition:

In 2008, the AMA added two sets of codes describing telephone services to patients: 99441–99443 for physicians making or receiving phone calls to/from patients and 98966–98968 for Non-Physician Practitioners (NPPs) making or receiving calls to/from patients. CPT® uses the term qualified nonphysician healthcare professional instead of NPP. (Codes 99371–99373 were deleted in 2008.) Medicare has given these new codes a status indicator of non-covered.

Explanation:

Physicians and NPPs spend considerable time talking to patients on the phone. They report diagnostic results, assess new symptoms, renew prescriptions and give advice. Historically, they were not paid for these services.

Codes: 99441–99443 and 98966–98968.

Coverage: Non-covered by Medicare.

Billing and coding rules:

Physicians are often frustrated by the inability to be paid for the enormous amount of time they spend on the phone. Since the inception of RBRVS, Medicare has considered phone calls to/from patients and about patients to be part of the pre and post work of another professional service. Similarly, most third party payers denied payment for phone calls, and their contracts did not allow the practice to bill the patient for the service.

The new codes have very specific definitions and their use is restricted both before and after another E/M service. The codes may not be billed if, as a result of the call, an E/M service is scheduled in the next 24 hours or for the first available urgent visit. They may not be reported for seven days after an E/M service.

Medicare published its regulation about phone calls in the Physician Fee Schedule in 1991.

Physician Fee Schedule Final Rule dated November 25, 1991, Vol 56, No. 227, page 59533:

"Although CPT® has codes for telephone calls, carriers must not make separate payment for telephone calls. Medicare's policy has always been and will continue to be that telephone calls are part of the physician work in the visit or service and that payment for the visit or service encompasses the payment for the telephone call. The work in the telephone calls is already included in the RVUs for the visit since it is part of the pre and post work of the service."

If the phone calls as described in the CPT® book are not related to an E/M service, then they can be billed to a Medicare patient. If the phone calls are related to an E/M service, they may not be billed to the patient. Although an ABN is not required for noncovered services, CMS recommends obtaining one. However, it isn't easy to obtain an ABN for a phone call prior to the phone call. Phone calls are usually unscheduled, and of course, the patient isn't there to sign an ABN.

If billing these services to Medicare patients, be sure they meet the criteria of the CPT® description, and that they are not pre or post work for an E/M.

Related issues:

Care Plan Oversight is one service which allows a physician to be paid for non-face-to-face time. The anti-coagulation management codes, 99363–99364, have a status indicator of bundled, and so may not be billed to the patient with or without a modifier.

As of this writing, CMS has not updated its Claims Processing Manual section about billing for telephone calls. It still prohibits billing for telephone calls as they were defined with codes 99371–99373, which were deleted in 2008.

Key Points:

- Review the billing rules carefully.
- These are time based codes, so document time in the medical record.
- Non-covered services may be billed to Medicare patients. Medicare will not pay for them.
- Check with your third party payers for coverage rules, and to see if your contract allows you to bill the patient.

Citations:

CPT® Changes: An Insider's View 2008

CPT® Assistant Mar 08:6

Time Based Codes

Definition:

Many types of service are time based, including psychiatry, physical medicine, and critical care. Therefore, the definition of some CPT® codes includes time.

Explanation:

When providing a service for which the definition of its CPT® code includes a time component, or when billing an E/M code based on time, you must document time in the medical record. You can also use time to select E/M codes if typical time is listed for that code in the CPT® book, and the visit is predominantly counseling and coordination of care. Document the total time of the visit, the fact that more than 50% of the visit was counseling and the nature of the counseling.

Codes:

Varied, including some E/M codes, discharge services, critical care, prolonged services, education services, psychiatry, and physical medicine.

Coverage: Not applicable.

Billing and coding rules:

For some services, the clinician can simply write the total time spent providing the service as the final sentence of the note, at the heading of the note, or on the form that documents the service. Psychiatrists often document this at the heading of the visit note. Physical therapists often use a form that describes the service parameters, and one of these is time. For critical care, the physician should document the total time spent in caring for the patient on a particular calendar date or during a 24 hour period. Document time in the medical record, not just on the billing record. Medicare requires start and stop time for prolonged services.

Many E/M codes can be billed using time as the determining factor for selecting the level of service. Time is the trump card when certain conditions are met, such as when more than 50% of the visit was spent in counseling or coordination of care. Here's how the CPT® book describes the content of counseling:

Counseling is discussion with patient and/or family regarding:
- Diagnostic results, impressions, recommended diagnostic studies
- Prognosis
- Risks and benefits of management
- Instructions for management
- Importance of compliance
- Risk factor reduction
- Patient and family education

Document:
- Total time for the visit
- Statement that more than 50% of the visit was counseling
- Description of the nature of the counseling

When using time to select an E/M service in the office or outpatient department, define total time as the time the clinician spends face-to-face with the patient. For hospital services, define the total time as the unit time. In order to bill hospital services based on time, more than 50% of the unit time must be spent in face-to-face counseling with the patient. You may not include staff time in the time spent; only the billing provider's time counts.

These definitions say, "with the patient and/or family." However, keep in mind that Medicare requires the clinician to have a face-to-face service with the beneficiary in order to bill for the service. You can not have a discussion with a patient's family member and bill Medicare for the service.

For some patients, however, the provider must spend an unusual amount of time treating and discussing their problems, above and beyond what is typical for the level of service provided. There are a set of add-on codes that may be used with office visits, outpatient consults, and home visits (99354–99355), and a set of codes that may be used with initial hospital services, subsequent hospital visits and inpatient consultations (99356–99357). These are called prolonged services codes and describe just that: a service that is prolonged beyond the usual.

These codes are a little tricky for providers. They require face-to-face direct patient contact with the billing provider, not a staff person. The prolonged service does not need to be continuous, but it must add up to 30 to 74 minutes more than the typical time for the service. That means the total time for prolonged services varies according to the base code of the service provided. Here's how the *Medicare Claims Processing Manual* describes it:

Prolonged services codes can be billed only if the total duration of all physician direct face-to-face service (including the visit) equals or exceeds the threshold time for the evaluation and management service the physician provided (typical time plus 30 minutes). If the total duration of direct face-to-face time does not equal or exceed the threshold time for the level of evaluation and management service the physician provided, the physician may not bill for prolonged services.

Why might a service be prolonged? Sometimes, the patient is unable to understand the problem or home care instructions without extensive and repeated explanations. A discussion with the patient might involve highly emotional issues that require longer than usual physician time. Or a patient may need to have a long discussion with a provider when weighing the risks and benefits of multiple treatment options for a serious illness.

Select a level of service based on the history, exam, and medical decision making documented. Then, if the total time exceeds the usual time for that E/M code by more than 30 minutes, bill using prolonged services. When billing for prolonged services, document total time spent. See the entry on prolonged services for more detailed information.

Related issues:

Clinicians are often reluctant to document time in the medical record, saying it's "cheesy," "tacky," or worse! However, if the definition of a code is time based, not documenting time results in no payment for the service.

Key points:

- Document time in the medical record when time is used to select the level of service.
- For E/M services in which time is the determining factor, document the total time of the visit, the fact that more than 50% was spent in counseling, and the nature of the counseling. Select your level of service based on the total time.
- For prolonged services, select the level of E/M code that you provided and documented. If your total time spent with the patient was 30 minutes more than the typical time, you may append a prolonged services code. Document the total time, and use the chart above to select the appropriate code.

- Document critical care time in the note.
- Document time in the discharge summary for the second level hospital discharge service.

See also: Critical care, prolonged services code, teaching physician rules for time based codes.

Citation:

> CMS, *Medicare Claims Processing Manual*, Pub. 100-04, Chapter 12, Section 30.6.15.1, http://www.cms.gov/Manuals/IOM/list.asp

Welcome to Medicare

Definition:

The Welcome to Medicare Visit or Initial Preventive Physical Exam (IPPE) is a one time benefit for new Medicare beneficiaries. The goal of this service is disease prevention, health promotion and education, counseling, and referral for covered preventive medicine services.

Explanation:

The Welcome to Medicare Visit was implemented as part of the Medicare Modernization Act passed in July of 2004. The benefit had an effective date of January 1st, 2005 and changes were made in 2009. Any Medicare beneficiary who became eligible for Medicare after that date was eligible for the service within the first twelve months of their benefit period.

Codes:

G0402 Welcome to Medicare visit; Diagnosis, V70.0 or medical diagnosis.

G0403 EKG with interpretation and report; Diagnosis, V70.0 or medical diagnosis.

G0404 Tracing only; Diagnosis same as above.

G0405 Report only; Diagnosis same as above.

Coverage:

This is a Medicare covered service only. Other payers typically do not pay for these codes. Effective January 1, 2009 the deductible was waived for G0402. The health care reform act provisions are not in rule form as of this writing. For services in 2010, the co-payment is still in effect for G0402.

Billing and coding rules:

This service is not your usual preventive service, and the definition of this service does not correspond to the visit described by CPT® codes 99381–99397. It differs from the annual preventive medicine exam and has specific requirements. Here's how the Internet Only Manual from Medicare describes the components of the IPPE:

> The initial preventive physical examination (IPPE), or "Welcome to Medicare Visit," is a preventive evaluation and management service (E/M) that includes: (1) review of the individual's medical and social history with attention to modifiable risk factors for disease

detection; (2) review of the individual's potential (risk factors) for depression or other mood disorders; (3) review of the individual's functional ability and level of safety; (4) a physical examination to include measurement of the individual's height, weight, blood pressure, a visual acuity screen, and other factors as deemed appropriate by the examining physician or qualified nonphysician practitioner (NPP); (5) performance and interpretation of an electrocardiogram (EKG) (optional as of January 1, 2009); (6) education, counseling, and referral, as deemed appropriate, based on the results of the review and evaluation services described in the previous five elements; and (7) education, counseling, and referral including a brief written plan (e.g., a checklist or alternative) provided to the individual for obtaining the appropriate screening and other preventive services, which are separately covered under Medicare Part B benefits.

As of January 1, 2009, the provider must calculate the Body Mass Index (BMI) and with the patient's permission, discuss end of life issues. This service may be performed by a physician, a nurse practitioner, a physician assistant, or a clinical nurse specialist.

The written plan should include education, counseling, and referral to any of these covered screening, immunization, or preventive services for which the patient is eligible:

- Pneumococcal, influenza and hepatitis B vaccines and their administration
- Screening mammography
- Screening pap smear and screening pelvic exams
- Prostate cancer screening services
- Colorectal cancer screening tests
- Diabetes outpatient self management training services
- Bone mass measurements
- Screening for glaucoma
- Medical nutrition therapy services for individuals with diabetes or renal disease
- Cardiovascular screening blood tests
- Diabetes screening tests

Related issues:

The provider is required to use screening tools for depression, hearing loss, activities of daily living, and safety that are approved by national specialty societies. The checkout for this visit can be very time consuming because it includes referrals for many preventive medicine services.

Key points:
- Be sure to use a form that includes all of the required elements. It is insufficient to use most history and physical forms that are in use for other preventive medicine services.
- A staff member or a patient may complete the screening components of this exam. The clinician must review the screening information and provide counseling, education, and referrals based on it.
- Education, counseling and referral based on the assessment are required.
- A written plan is required for the preventive medicine services covered by Medicare.

See also: Preventive medicine services, wellness visits

Citations:

Medlearn Matters Web site. 2006. Available at: http://www.cms.gov/MLNMattersArticles

Medlearn Matters Number: MM3638, Release date December 22, 2004.

CMS, *Medicare Claims Processing Manual*, Pub. 100-04, Chapter 12, Section 30.6.1.1, http://www.cms.gov/Manuals/IOM/list.asp

CMS, *CMS Manual System*, Pub. 100-04, Transmittal 446, Change Request 3637, January 21, 2005.

CMS, *CMS Manual System*, Pub. 100-04, Transmittal 417, Change Request 3638, December, 22, 2004.

https://www.cms.gov/MLNProducts/35_PreventiveServices.asp

Wellness Visits (Also Known As "Personalized Prevention Plan Services")

Definition:

The healthcare reform bill that passed in spring of 2010 (Patient Protection and Affordable Care Act) mandated coverage of annual wellness exams for Medicare patients. The proposed Physician Fee Schedule released in June of 2010 provided a draft version of the benefit, which will be finalized after this book goes to press at the end of 2010. All of the information in this article is from the proposed rule, and will be finalized after the book is printed. Check with CMS or your Medicare Contractor for the final provisions.

Explanation:

Medicare does not cover routine services. At its inception, it was conceived as a program that provided care for illness and injuries and routine care was specifically excluded. Over the years, Congress had added coverage for screening services to Medicare. This new wellness benefit is another covered service. It joins the Welcome to Medicare visit, and is similar in scope to that service.

Codes:

The HCPCS (not CPT®) codes will be released in late 2010. Medicare will not pay for 99387, 99397, or any codes in the preventive medicine series from 99381–99397. *Those will remain non-covered, routine services!*

The wellness visits will be defined as initial and subsequent visits, and will not be defined as new or established patient services.

Coverage:

Which Medicare patients are eligible for the wellness visit? Patients who have been on Medicare for over 12 months and who have not received either a Welcome to Medicare visit or an annual wellness exam in the past 12 months. That is, during the first 12 months of enrollment in Medicare, a patient is eligible *only* for the Welcome to Medicare visit. And, the initial wellness visit may only be provided once in a patient's lifetime, not once per physician or Non-Physician Practitioner. Patients will be eligible for the subsequent wellness visit one year after the initial service.

Patients who have been on Medicare for longer than 12 months are no longer eligible for the Welcome to Medicare visit, and are eligible for the initial wellness visit.

Billing and coding rules:

The rules described below are from the proposed Physician Fee Schedule released in the summer of 2010. Check with CMS or your Medicare Contractor for the final rule at the end of 2010. There may be changes based on comments CMS receives.

During the first 12 months of Medicare enrollment, a patient is eligible only for the Welcome to Medicare visit. Assuming the patient receives that service, the patient is eligible for the initial wellness visit one year after receiving the Welcome to Medicare visit. What does that wellness visit look like? Well, it's not your daughter's preventive medicine service. This once in a lifetime benefit is defined by Medicare as the development of a personalized prevention plan service. It requires:

- Taking or updating the individual's medical and family history
- Establishing a list of all current providers and suppliers of medical care to the patient
- The physical exam requires: height, weight, body mass index (BMI) calculation (or waist circumference), BP and "other routine measurements as deemed appropriate"
- Detection of any cognitive impairment that the individual may have. This may be done by direct observation, with consideration of information from medical records, patient reports, or concerns raised by family members.
- Review of the potential for depression *based on use of appropriate screening instrument* (This is also required in the Welcome to Medicare visit)
- Review of individual's functional ability and level of safety. This can be based on direct observation, or use of screening questionnaire regarding hearing impairment, ability to perform activities of daily living, fall risk and home safety. (The Welcome to Medicare visit requires screening for these issues with an accepted instrument or tool.)
- **Written** screening schedule, such as a checklist, for the next 5-10 years based on recommendations of the US Preventive Task Force and Advisory Committee on Immunization Practices, and the individual's health status, screening history, and age-appropriate covered Medicare services.

- A list of risk factors and conditions for which primary, secondary or tertiary interventions are recommended or are underway, including mental health conditions or risk factors or conditions identified through the visit.
- A list of treatment options and their associated risks and benefits
- Furnishing of personalized health advice and referral, as appropriate to health education or preventive counseling programs aimed at reducing identified risk and improving self management including weight loss, smoking cessation, fall prevention and nutrition
- And, any other element determined as appropriate by the Secretary of Health and Human Services through the National Coverage Determination process

What will a physician be paid for developing this personalized prevention service? CMS is proposing to assign the same RVUs as for a level four new patient visit, 99204. In 2010, 99204 had a non-facility, national rate of $155.

Medicare patients will be eligible for a subsequent wellness visit one year after they received the initial wellness visit. This visit requires:

- Updating the medical and family history.
- Updating the list of current providers or suppliers of medical care to patient.
- The physical exam required is only: weight, BP and "other routine measurements as deemed appropriate" (Height and BMI calculation are not required).
- Detection of cognitive function.
- Updating the **written** screening schedule established at initial visit.
- Updating the list of risk factors and conditions for which treatment was recommended.
- Furnishing personalized health advice and referral, as appropriate, to health education or preventive counseling programs aimed at reducing identified risk and improving self management including weight loss, smoking cessation, fall prevention and nutrition.

CMS is proposing that this second service be paid at the rate of a level four established patient visit. At least one specialty society has commented that this rate is too low. 99214 has a non-facility RVUs of 2.71 and pays about $100 at the national rate.

Will a physician be permitted to report an office visit on the same day as the wellness visit? Here's what the proposed rule says about that: "We believe this scenario would be uncommon, and we expect that no components of an encounter attributable to the annual wellness visit would be used in determining the level of a separate E/M visit that would also be reported."

Related issues:

Patients who receive their care from more than one physician (perhaps in two states) will present a challenge. The visits are per beneficiary, not per physician. Patients will be expecting to receive an "annual physical." This service does not correspond to the CPT® definition of a preventive medicine service. Routine care remains non-covered. If a physician practice provides an annual physical exam, as defined by CPT® codes 99381–99397, it will be denied, and the physician office may not resubmit it with the wellness visit codes.

Key points:

- Watch for the release of the codes and the final definitions of the service in late 2010.
- Don't be confused into thinking this is an annual exam or preventive service as defined by CPT® codes. This is a "personalized prevention plan service" and will be defined by CMS with HCPCS codes.
- Visits are not defined as new or established, but as initial and subsequent.
- The initial exam is like the Welcome to Medicare visit in many ways, and both are a "once in a lifetime" benefit to patients.
- Patients who are newly enrolled in Medicare are eligible for the Welcome to Medicare visit in the first 12 months, not the initial wellness visit.
- Patients will expect to receive the service as a covered benefit.

See also: Welcome to Medicare

Citations:

The final rule will be released by Medicare in late 2010. This information is from the proposed rule.

Guide to Acronyms

A/R........	Accounts Receivable
AAO-HNS..	American Academy of Otolaryngology-Head and Neck Surgery
ABN.......	Advance Beneficiary Notice
AMA.......	American Medical Association
ASC	Ambulatory Surgical Center
CERT	Comprehensive Error Rate Testing
CLIA.......	Clinical Laboratory Improvement Amendment
CMS	Centers for Medicare & Medicaid Services
CPO.......	Care Plan Oversight
CT	Computerized Axial Tomography
CWF.......	Common Working File
DMERC....	Durable Medical Equipment Regional Carriers
DPA.......	Darbepoetin alpha
E/M	Evaluation and Management
ED	Emergency Department
ENT.......	Ears Nose and Throat
EPO.......	Epoetin alpha
EPSDT.....	Early Periodic Screening, Diagnostic and Treatment
GPCI	Geographic Practice Cost Index
HCFA......	Health Care Financing Administration
HCPCS	Healthcare Common Procedures Coding System
HHA	Home Health Agency
HPI	History of the Present Illness
IPPE.......	Initial Preventive Physical Exam
LCD.......	Local Coverage Determination
LMRP	Local Medical Review Policies
MDM......	Medical Decision Making
MGMA	Medical Group Management Association
MMSE.....	Mini Mental Status Exam
MPFSDB ...	Medicare Physician Fee Schedule Data Base
MPSDB	Medicare Physician Schedule Data Base

MRI . . . . Magnetic Resonance Imaging

NCD . . . . . . National Coverage Determination

NPI . . . . National Provider Identifier

NPP . . . . Non-Physician Practitioner

OBS . . . . Observation Billing Status

OIG . . . . Office of the Inspector General

OR . . . . Operating Room

POS . . . . Place of Service

PPM . . . . Provider-Performed Microscopy

PVRP . . . . . . Physician Voluntary Reporting Program

RVU . . . . Relative Value Unit

SNF . . . . Skilled Nursing Facility

UPIN . . . . . . Unique Physician Identification Number